FISH AND RIVER POLLUTION

Frontispiece. Apparatus developed by the Ministry of Agriculture, Fisheries and Food for standard toxicity tests on fish. Up to 18 dilutions of an effluent or toxic substance can be tested simultaneously; 10 small fish at each dilution. The apparatus controls the concentration, temperature, oxygen content and pH, *and the quality of the dilution water*

FISH AND RIVER

POLLUTION

J. R. ERICHSEN JONES, Ph.D., D.Sc.

Department of Zoology
University College of Wales
Aberystwyth

WASHINGTON

BUTTERWORTHS

1964

U.S.A.:   BUTTERWORTH INC.
                   WASHINGTON, D.C.: 7235 Wisconsin Avenue, 14

ENGLAND: BUTTERWORTH & CO. (PUBLISHERS) LTD.
                   LONDON: 88 Kingsway, W.C.2

AUSTRALIA: BUTTERWORTH & CO. (AUSTRALIA) LTD.
                   SYDNEY: 6/8 O'Connell Street
                   MELBOURNE: 473 Bourke Street
                   BRISBANE: 240 Queen Street

CANADA: BUTTERWORTH & CO. (CANADA) LTD.
                   TORONTO: 1367 Danforth Avenue, 6

NEW ZEALAND: BUTTERWORTH & CO. (NEW ZEALAND) LTD.
                   WELLINGTON: 49/51 Ballance Street
                   AUCKLAND: 35 High Street

SOUTH AFRICA: BUTTERWORTH & CO. (SOUTH AFRICA) LTD.
                   DURBAN: 33/35 Beach Grove

Suggested U.D.C. No.: 628.515:597

Made and printed in Great Britain by
William Clowes and Sons, Limited, London and Beccles

CONTENTS

ABBREVIATIONS

atm	atmosphere (pressure) = 14·7 lb./in.^{2}
B.Th.U.	British Thermal Unit
cm^3	cubic centimetres
g	grammes
h	hours
l.	litres
M	Molar, i.e. a solution containing the molecular weight in grammes of a substance per litre of the solution
m.	miles
mg	milligrammes
ml.	millilitres
mm Hg	millimetres of mercury (760 mm Hg = 1 atm)
N	Normal, i.e. a solution containing 1 gramme equivalent of substance, or amount of substance equivalent to 1·008 grammes of hydrogen, per litre of solution
p.p.m.	parts per million (or milligrammes per litre)
y	year
<	less than
>	greater than

PREFACE

THERE IS a very considerable literature dealing with river pollution, but most of the information is scattered through very many scientific and technical journals and comparatively few books on the subject have been written. In 1957 Dr. Louis Klein's *Aspects of River Pollution* was published. This dealt with river pollution mainly from the standpoint of the chemist but Dr. Klein invited me to contribute to it a chapter dealing with the effects of pollution on fish, and Mr. H. A. Hawkes of the Birmingham Tame and Rea District Drainage Board contributed a chapter on the biological aspects of river pollution. For Volume II of the second edition of Dr. Klein's work I revised and enlarged the chapter on fish and in the course of this work it appeared to me that a fuller treatment of the subject was desirable. This book is the result, and the writing of it has been a very pleasant and absorbing task. In it I have attempted to summarize and review the experimental and field research that has been carried out on the effects of pollution on fish, and to bring together as much as possible of the useful data. While the treatment is, I trust, thoroughly scientific, I have endeavoured to avoid chemical and mathematical complexities as far as possible, in the hope that the book may prove of interest not only to those whose interest in the subject is what may be termed 'professional' but also to fishermen and naturalists. In its 16 chapters I have devoted very little space to the more purely chemical side of the subject; for this the reader is referred to the very comprehensive treatment by Dr. Klein. The book deals entirely with fish, and for information on the effects of pollution on plants and invertebrates he may read the excellent account given by Dr. H. B. N. Hynes in *The Biology of Polluted Waters*, published by the Liverpool University Press in 1960.

Much of the experimental work done on the effects of pollution on fish requires little in the way of apparatus. Lest the amateur scientist may be tempted to carry out experiments, it may not be inappropriate for me to point out that fish, being vertebrates, are animals protected by the laws relating to experiments upon living animals, and that in Britain, and most other countries, experiments upon them calculated to cause pain or suffering must not be performed without licence from the proper authorities.

For permission to reproduce data and text-figures I would like to

PREFACE

thank Dr. C. M. Tarzwell of the Robert A. Taft Sanitary Engineering Center at Cincinnati, Dr. J. R. Brett of the Biological Station at Nanaimo, British Columbia, Drukkerij 'Volharding', the Academic Press, and the editors of the *Journal of Experimental Biology*, the *Annals of Applied Biology*, the *Water and Waste Treatment Journal*, the *International Journal of Air and Water Pollution*, the *Proceedings of the Society for Water Treatment and Examination*, the *Transactions of the American Fisheries Society*, the *Journal of the Fisheries Research Board of Canada*, and *University of Toronto Studies*. I would like, also, to thank Her Majesty's Stationery Office for permission to reproduce data and text-figures from *Water Pollution Research*, and for the frontispiece. I have been fortunate in having access to, in the Biology Department Library at Aberystwyth, a complete set of the *D.S.I.R. Water Pollution Abstracts*, and I am grateful to the library staff who have been of great assistance in obtaining for me books and journals from other libraries.

It was the late Professor T. A. Stephenson, F.R.S., who, when he held the chair at the Department of Zoology at Aberystwyth, first suggested that I should write this book, and I am very grateful for his advice and encouragement. Finally I would like to record my thanks to Dr. B. A. Southgate, the staff at the Water Pollution Research Laboratory at Alresford and all the many other scientists who have sent me reprints and literature; their help has made the writing of this book so much easier.

February, 1964   J.R.E.J.

INTRODUCTION: A BRIEF HISTORY OF EXPERIMENTAL WORK ON THE EFFECTS OF POLLUTION ON FISH

IN LAGLER's *Freshwater Fishery Biology*[1] the bio-assay of a pollutant is presented as a classroom exercise. The student is given a number of fish and a suitable toxic chemical. Various concentrations of this are prepared and their action on the fish is studied; the object being to work out the tolerance limit, the concentration the fish can survive for a suitable specified period. This would seem to be a very simple and rather obvious method of investigation but experimental methods for the study of the effects of pollution on fish took a long time to develop, and for a long period after the harmful results of pollution had become apparent, scientific study of its effects on fish was negligible though there was no shortage of opinion and conjecture. Some of the first experiments on the action of chemical substances on fish were made nearly a hundred years ago by Penny and Adams[2] who, in 1867, examined the River Leven, a tributary of the Clyde, which was then polluted by effluents from a dye-works. They decided to carry out some laboratory tests of the effects on fish of the various chemicals present, and it is interesting to find that they selected two fish types for their study: the minnow, on account of 'the fine sensibility it evinces towards all kinds of disturbing influences' and the goldfish, whose sluggish nature and tenacity of life permitted sufficient time for observing the action of poisonous substances. Some of their work was carried out with water from the polluted river; other experiments were made with solutions of the acids, salts and other substances present in the effluents. In all they made 428 experiments with 71 chemicals.

After this very promising beginning the experimental investigation of water pollution progressed very slowly for some time. In the U.S.A. little work of importance was done until about 1912, when the studies of V. E. Shelford and M. M. Wells began to be published. At this time chemists and biologists were beginning to be very interested in bio-assay and in 1917 Powers[3] published his well-known paper 'The goldfish as a test-animal in the study of toxicity'. This paper was probably not intended, at the time, to have any direct bearing on the study of pollution, for most of the substances studied by Powers are not pollutants, but it soon proved to be very interesting to workers in this field when they began to study the relation between survival time and concentration.

In 1919 Kathleen Carpenter, whose work is discussed in Chapter 5, began studying the rivers of west Wales, where the mining of lead and zinc had been a serious cause of pollution for a considerable period. For a long time her whole attention was concentrated on the general nature of the affected rivers and their fauna and flora. She had seen the reports of Penny and Adams and it seems strange that about four years elapsed before experimental work on the problem was started, but it was 1923 before she began work with fish cages and her experiments with laboratory-prepared solutions of lead salts were not carried out until some time after this. The war of 1914–18 had brought about a considerable aggravation of the troubles produced by water pollution and interest in experimental work was developing. The Ministry of Agriculture and Fisheries Experimental Station at Alresford was, at this time, concerned with the effects of tars and phenolic substances on fish. German papers dealing with this problem reached England after the war[4] and the importance of experimental work with solutions of polluting substances and fish of various types was beginning to be appreciated. The effect of pollution by sewage and other oxygen-removing matter had also attracted much attention by then and work had begun on the oxygen requirements of fish and their capacity for tolerating low oxygen tensions.

An important paper on bio-assay which appeared in 1927 is that by Belding[5]. This is one of the first critical analyses of the conditions required for successful experiments with polluting substances. Belding pointed out that a number of factors might influence the results, including the species of fish used, its sex, age, size and general physical condition, the size of the solution container and the volume of the solution, the oxygen content of the water and the temperature. Steinmann's *Toxicologie der Fische*[6] appeared in 1928, but this work appears to have attracted very little attention in English-speaking countries. Steinmann used trout for his experiments and tested a considerable range of substances, including oxalic, lactic and tannic acid, nicotine, phenol, cresol, benzene, toluene and the chlorides or sulphates of iron, aluminium, calcium and zinc. In studies with carbon dioxide, hydrochloric and sulphuric acid, ammonia and chlorine he made records of changes in the breathing frequency of the fish and their rate of heartbeat.

In 1937 the classic paper 'Detection and measurement of stream

2

pollution' by M. M. Ellis was published. This work, discussed in many chapters of this book, was soon recognized as a considerable advance in the organized study of pollution problems. Ellis's study is important on three counts: first, he laid emphasis on exhaustive study of environmental conditions—thus his analysis of the oxygen conditions necessary for the survival of fish included 6,000 determinations of oxygen tensions in rivers and streams of the U.S.A.; secondly, he gathered together and discussed most of the knowledge then available about the different ways in which fish may be killed by polluting substances, and thirdly he carried out a considerable number of experiments on the effects of acids, bases, salts and other substances on fish, using hard and soft water. However, Ellis seems to have had somewhat vague ideas about what is implied by the term 'lethal limit', and while his experiments with most substances covered a very wide concentration range, the concentrations were too widely spaced for the lethal limit to be indicated with any degree of accuracy. Thus in his work with metallic salts he seems to have employed only concentrations of 1,000, 100, 10 and 1 p.p.m. and while the infinity sign is frequently inserted in the data to record the survival time there is no clear indication as to what this means. For example, in the case of ferrous sulphate the survival time of goldfish at a concentration of 1,000 p.p.m. is given as 2–10 h. The next concentration tested is 100 p.p.m. and the survival time in this case is given as ∞.

Most of the papers directly concerned with pollution problems are published in the journals of applied science but a considerable amount of important research dealing with the effects of chemical and physical agents upon fish has been carried out by investigators whose aim is the advancement of pure biological science, and their results are to be found in periodicals such as the *Journal of Experimental Biology*. In the past 20 years our understanding of the effects of pollutants on fish has been improved to a very great extent by the advances that have been made in the study of the physiology of these animals. Thus the development of apparatus for measuring the oxygen consumption of fish under conditions of sustained activity has presented the problem of oxygen-removing effluents in a completely new light and the intensive study of the thermal relations of fish, begun by scientists at Toronto, has enabled the problems of thermal pollution to be understood. Some fish have special physiological characteristics which make them very resistant to pollution of certain types. Thus some species are adapted for obtaining oxygen from the atmosphere and so are more or less unaffected by depletion of the dissolved oxygen. An interesting example recently described is the comparative immunity of the goldfish to carbon monoxide. This gas is extremely poisonous

3

FISH AND RIVER POLLUTION

to man and many other animals because it combines with the haemoglobin of the blood corpuscles, robbing the blood of its capacity for
transporting oxygen. Anthony[7] has shown that the goldfish has a
remarkable resistance to CO poisoning; this is because it is not completely dependent upon haemoglobin for oxygen transport and when
practically all its haemoglobin has been converted into carboxyhaemoglobin its blood plasma carries in solution enough oxygen to
permit not only existence but a fair degree of activity. The literature
on water pollution has become very extensive but is well reviewed by
the *Water Pollution Abstracts* published by the Department of Scientific
and Industrial Research. Many papers are summarized in the
Limnology and *Wildlife Management–Aquatic* sections of *Biological Abstracts*, published by Biological Abstracts of Philadelphia, and the titles
of papers dealing with the ecology and physiology of fish are given in
the *Zoological Record*.

REFERENCES

[1] Lagler, K. F. *Freshwater Fishery Biology.* 1952. Dubuque, Iowa; Wm.
C. Brown
[2] Penny, C. and Adams, C. Fourth Report, Royal Commission on Pollution of Rivers in Scotland, Vol. 2, *Evidence*, 377–91, London (1863)
[3] Powers, E. B. The goldfish (*Carassius carassius*) as a test-animal in the
study of toxicity. *Illinois biol. Monogr.*, 4 (1917), 127–93
[4] *River Pollution and Fisheries*: Non-technical report on the work during 1925
of the Standing Committee on River Pollution. 1926. London;
H.M.S.O.
[5] Belding, D. L. Toxicity experiments with fish in reference to trade waste
pollution. *Trans. Amer. Fish. Soc.*, 57 (1927) 100–19
[6] Steinmann, P. Toxicologie der fische. In *Handbuch der Binnenfischerei
Mitteleuropas*, Band VI. 1928. Stuttgart; E. Schweizerbart'sche
Verlagsbuchhandlung
[7] Anthony, E. H. Survival of goldfish in presence of carbon monoxide.
J. exp. Biol. 38 (1961) 109–25

FISH AND OXYGEN: POLLUTION BY OXYGEN-REDUCING EFFLUENTS

WHEN sewage, milk washings and other effluents containing organic matter are discharged into rivers and streams much of the material they carry in suspension and solution is broken down by the micro-organisms present in stream water, a process which involves using up the dissolved oxygen. If this is removed faster than it can be replaced by natural means the concentration of dissolved oxygen falls. In-organic substances that are readily oxidized, such as sulphites and ferrous salts, can produce a similar effect. Normally, streams are kept well aerated by the movement of the water and the photo-synthesis of the plants and a certain amount of organic pollution can be tolerated; in fact, some addition of organic matter can be beneficial as this can enrich the food supply, and many of the invertebrate animals of the stream-bed feed upon the mixture of mineral matter and amorphous organic matter called detritus, which accumulates on the bottom. A serious degree of organic pollution results in a deple-tion of the oxygen supply which is harmful or lethal to fish. Many examples could be quoted of the effects of heavy sewage pollution on the fish fauna of streams. A typical case is that described by Katz and Gaufin[1] who made a series of collections in a stream in Ohio. In the septic areas below the outfall of the effluent no fish were observed or collected. Two miles away, in the recovery zone, eight species were represented; at 3 m. many more individuals of 12 species were found and the numbers and variety increased steadily with the improvement in the condition of the water so that 32 species could be found 4·4 m. below the outfall.

In grossly polluted septic zones the oxygen content may be reduced to zero and this may happen in the largest rivers. Thus Wiebe[2] found that many samples of water taken from the Mississippi below Minneapolis contained none. Under these conditions the process of decomposition of organic matter is taken over by anaerobic bacteria and putrefaction may lead to the production of hydrogen sulphide and other noxious end products, the effects of which will be discussed in later chapters. This chapter deals with the way the life of fish is determined by the oxygen content of their environment.

5

Most fish are adapted for aquatic respiration only. Water taken in through the mouth is passed through the gill chambers to be expelled through the long openings behind the gill covers or opercula. In teleost fish (the more advanced types with bony skeletons) the flow of water over the gills is continuous for almost the whole of the respiratory cycle[3]. In its passage the water gives up oxygen to the blood and takes away carbon dioxide; the oxygen is transported around the body by haemoglobin in the blood corpuscles as in other vertebrates but the blood system is simpler than that of mammals; in its circuit of the body the blood passes through the heart once only and this has only a single auricle and a single ventricle, not two of each as in the four-chambered heart of warm-blooded animals. From the heart, which lies mid-ventrally between the pectoral fins, the blood is driven forward along a median ventral aorta; this gives off a series of afferent arteries to the gills. From the gills the blood is collected by efferent arteries and the arterial system then distributes it to all parts of the body, the return to the heart being made through a system of veins and sinuses. In this venous system there appear to be no valves and it is stated that if an eel is held head upwards its heart rapidly becomes empty of blood[4]. The blood pressure in the arteries is low and the circulation slow compared with that of mammals[5].

Some fish living in swampy environments where the oxygen concentration of the water may be very low have acquired accessory organs for breathing atmospheric oxygen or make use of the alimentary canal for respiration. Thus *Clarias lazera*, the 'clara', a tropical catfish, has a pair of supra-branchial chambers containing highly vascular, arborescent organs which serve for aerial respiration[6]. Air is swallowed and passes into these chambers, later passing out under the opercula; these fish can live out of water for periods of up to 30 h. In *Ancistrus anisitsi*, from the swamps of the Paraguayan Chaco, the stomach is usually filled with air and is respiratory and in *Hoplosternum littorale* and *Callichthys callichthys*, from the same environment, a portion of the intestine is kept filled with air for the same purpose[7]. The common loach *Nemacheilus barbatula* is also said to be able to live in water containing little or no oxygen by swallowing bubbles of air which pass along the gut. Other methods of utilizing atmospheric oxygen include the development of a respiratory epithelium in the pharynx, modification of the swim bladder so that swallowed air can be passed into it and it can function as a lung, and the use of the skin as a respiratory organ; this is seen in the eel which, at low temperatures, can obtain all the oxygen it needs by cutaneous respiration. Finally the gills of some fish have become adapted for aerial respiration but

FISH AND OXYGEN

this condition is very rare and seems to involve a great enlargement of the respiratory chambers [7].

A great deal of experimental work has been done on the physiology of respiration in fish and for a recent review the reader may be referred to that by Fry [8]. Van Dam [9] devised a method for studying respiration in the trout and other fish, which is shown in *Figure 1*. It will be seen that the animal is enclosed within two tubes, K_1 and K_2. Thin rubber diaphragms, H and M, fit accurately around the body; M is in front of and H behind the opercular openings so that all the water passed through the gill chambers is delivered through the tube R and can be measured and analysed. Van Dam showed that at 10–12° C

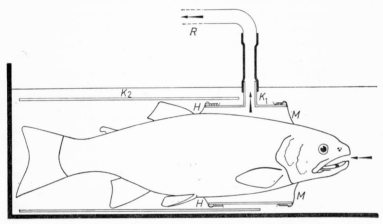

Figure 1. Van Dam's apparatus for studying respiration in fish
(After Van Dam [9], by courtesy of Drukkerij 'Volharding'.)

a rainbow trout 40 cm in length and weighing 900 g will perform about 90 breathing movements per minute when at rest, passing about 8 l. of water per hour. Each breathing movement therefore involves the swallowing of about 1·5 ml. The passage of water through the gill chambers is rapid but a high proportion of the oxygen is taken up. In normal, quiet breathing 80 per cent of the oxygen may be taken up by the blood; this proportion is referred to as the 'utilization'. Exertion and excitement bring about a quickening of the breathing, when the utilization will fall to 75 per cent or less, and violent exertion may result in a fivefold increase in the amount of water passing through the respiratory apparatus. Under these conditions more oxygen is obtained but the system is much less efficient as the utilization may now be only 50 per cent.

An apparatus of this type is mainly useful for the study of fish under

7

conditions of rest and it can furnish a great deal of information about the way the oxygen consumption is influenced by the oxygen concentration of the water supplied, by its temperature, by its carbon dioxide content, by variations in diet, by starvation and acclimatization to various conditions. If we are only interested in the amount of oxygen consumed by the animal, and measurements of the utilization and ventilation (the volume of water passed through the gill chambers) are not required, a basically simpler apparatus will serve. In this the fish is confined in a glass tube into which it fits comfortably and through which a current of water passes at a uniform speed. The oxygen content of the water flowing in at the head end of the tube is measured and also that of the water leaving the tube. The difference, when the rate of flow is known, can give the oxygen consumption. Though basically simple, this apparatus can become somewhat complicated under practical conditions. It is necessary to control the temperature and to regulate the flow of water very exactly. The water must flow at such a rate that the fish removes an amount of oxygen that can be measured with accuracy, but the amount of oxygen removed must not be so great as to alter the animal's rate of oxygen consumption. When the water supplied to the fish is saturated with oxygen the samples drawn off for analysis will not tend to pick up oxygen from the air to any serious extent, but when water of low oxygen content is being used for the experiment precautions must be taken to prevent the samples from coming into contact with the air, such as collecting them under oil. Apparatus may be included for supplying water of a constant, predetermined oxygen concentration; Shelford[10] devised such an arrangement and a fractionating column for the purpose has been described by Fry[11]. In some cases it is preferable to confine the fish in a small 'respiration chamber' through which water of known oxygen content is passed at a steady speed until the fish has become accustomed to the conditions. The flow is then stopped for a suitable period of time, sufficient for the fish to make a measurable reduction in the oxygen content of the water in the chamber, and at the end of the period a sample is drawn off for analysis[12]. This type of apparatus (*Figure 2*) is very suitable for studying the effect of toxic solutions. When making measurements of the oxygen consumption of fish it may be necessary to detect and record periods of activity. For this Spoor[13] devised an 'activity detector' (*Figure 3*). A light paddle freely suspended in the water of the experiment chamber is very sensitive to any disturbance set up by movements of the fish. Movement of the paddle will complete an electrical circuit and the frequency and duration of periods of activity can be recorded automatically.

For the study of the physiology of fish under conditions of continuous activity an apparatus of a different type is used. This was devised by Black, Fry and Scott[14] and improved by Fry and Hart[15] and by Job[16]. The basis of the apparatus is a rotating annular chamber, (*Figure 4*). The outer wall is of glass to permit observation of the fish;

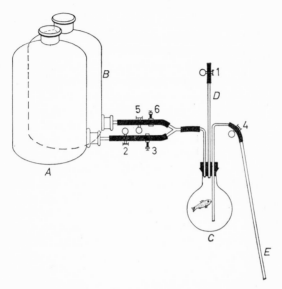

Figure 2. Apparatus for comparative studies on the oxygen consumption of fish. Water from aspirator A is run through the respiration flask C for some time; a sample is taken at E and its oxygen content measured. Then the flow is stopped by closing pinch-clip 2. After a suitable time interval pinch-clip 1 is opened to admit air through D and a sample of water is drawn off at E. The oxygen content of this is determined and the difference between this and that of the first sample is a measure of the amount used by the fish. After two or three trials a series of comparative determinations can be made with water of a different nature or a toxic solution supplied from aspirator B. Screw-clips 3 and 6 are to regulate the rate of flow. 4, 5: pinch-clips. For further details see Reference 12

(By courtesy of the *Journal of Experimental Biology*.)

the bottom and inner walls can be of metal or plastic. A fish is placed in the trough and this is set rotating. The fish will usually swim against the moving water; it may orientate itself in a fixed position by reference to objects on the test bench and may be helped in this by placing conspicuous objects near the outer glass wall[17].

By varying the speed of rotation of the 'fish wheel' a suitable subject

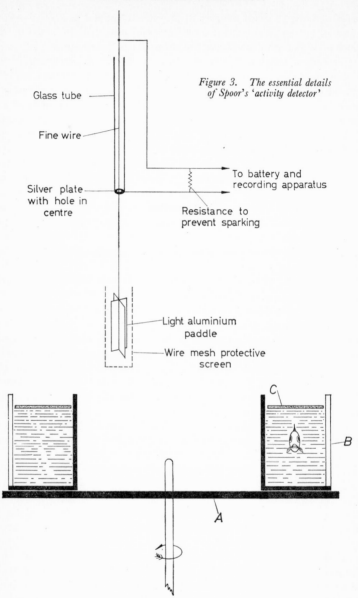

Glass tube

Fine wire

Silver plate
with hole in
centre

*Figure 3.   The essential details
of Spoor's 'activity detector'*

To battery and
recording apparatus

Resistance to
prevent sparking

Light aluminium
paddle

Wire mesh protective
screen

C

B

A

*Figure 4.   Basic arrangement for studying the physiology of fish under conditions of
continuous activity. A turntable.   B outer glass wall of rotating circular trough.
C loose, floating cover*

may be made to swim steadily at any desired speed up to the maximum of which it is capable. When the object of the study is to determine the rate at which the animal can swim under different conditions of temperature or the time for which it can maintain a certain pace there is no need for the surface of the water to be covered, but for measurements of the respiration rate the surface of the water must be cut off from contact with the air, otherwise the amount of oxygen taken up by the animal cannot be measured with accuracy. A loosely fitting floating cover can be used[15] or a rubber gasket[16]. Samples of water for determination of the oxygen content are withdrawn with a pipette. When the chamber is set rotating the water does not move at the same speed; its speed in relation to the speed of rotation of the chamber can be determined by observing the rate at which a small ball of cotton wool is carried around under the conditions of the experiment[17]. If the object of the experiment is to measure the oxygen consumption under conditions of maximum activity the actual speed of movement of the water need not be measured; the wheel is set to turn at a rate which compels the fish to exert itself to the utmost in order to maintain its position. It may require occasional encouragement by stimulation with a glass rod. Electric shocks can be used for stimulation, introduced through a ring commutator and four diametrically placed electrodes on the floor of the rotating chamber. Low, steady speeds can be induced by rotating the wheel so that the fish is carried backwards over a striped background; usually it will begin swimming to keep station and the speed can be increased until the fish just begins to fall back[18]. Some further details of apparatus and methods used for the study of respiration in fish follow later in this chapter.

Fish are poikilothermic or 'cold blooded' but their metabolic rate at normal temperatures does not compare too badly with that of warm-blooded animals. Some comparative figures for the oxygen consumption of an active fish (the trout), sluggish fish (eel and goldfish) and some representative invertebrates, birds and mammals, are given in Table 1. It will be seen that the oxygen consumption of the trout at 14·7° C is similar to that of the horse, the sheep and man, whose body temperatures are much higher, but falls far short of that of an active bird, the sparrow.

Most of the data in Table 1 apply to animals in a state of rest. In all animals the respiration rate increases with activity but the extent to which it can rise varies greatly with different types. The oxygen consumption of an insect in the full activity of flight may be over a hundred times its value at rest. In man the oxygen intake at rest is about 250 cm³/min; running steadily at 10 m.p.h. brings it up to

Table 1.   Oxygen Consumption of the Trout, Goldfish, Eel and Some
Other Representative animals*

Animal	cm³ O₂/g/h	Temp. °C
Jelly-fish (*Aurelia*)	0·0034–0·005	13–15
Starfish (*Asterias*)	0·03	15
Leech (*Hirudo*)	0·023	13·5
Mussel (*Mytilus*)	0·0549	22·3
Crayfish (*Astacus*)	0·04	?
Butterfly (*Vanessa*) at rest . . .	0·6	20
„ „ flying . . .	100·0	20
Eel	0·04	16·5
Goldfish	0·07	14·4
Trout	0·22	14·7
Sparrow	6·7	—
Horse	0·25	—
Sheep	0·34	—
Man	0·16–0·33	—
Dog	0·83	—

* The data are taken from Heilbrunn[19].

3,600 cm³/min and maximum oxygen consumption is about 4,000 cm³/min, or 16 times the resting rate[20]. In fish the maximum is about four times the resting rate[8]. Here, however, it should be noted that the resting respiration rates for fish determined by different workers differ quite considerably. Thus Van Dam[9] found the resting rate for the trout to be about 0·047 cm³ O₂/g/h, a much lower value than that given by Heilbrunn[19]. The size of the animal is an important factor, for the oxygen consumption of small fish, weight for weight, is greater than that of large ones. It is possible that some experiments have been carried out with the fish not in a state of complete rest. Wells[21] has shown that a fish may have to be kept in the respiration apparatus for up to 24 h before its metabolic rate settles down to the minimum value.

At rest or in activity the oxygen consumption of a fish increases rapidly as the temperature goes up. Van Dam[9], for example, found that raising the temperature from 11·6° C to 19·4° C resulted in the oxygen consumption of the rainbow trout being more than doubled and Gardner[22] obtained similar results with trout, grayling, eels and pike. Nature would have made life easier for fish if she could have arranged things so that the amount of oxygen water can hold in solution increased with rising temperatures. Actually, of course, the solubility of oxygen in water decreases with a rise in temperature and at boiling point all gases are expelled. On consulting the textbooks of inorganic chemistry it is found that the solubility of oxygen in water is 4 per cent at normal temperatures but this statement may mislead for it applies to water in contact with pure oxygen. When water is in equilibrium with *air* at atmospheric pressure it is in contact with a gas mixture in which the partial pressure of the oxygen is only about one-fifth of an atmosphere and so the amount it will dissolve is much less. At 4° C water saturated with air contains about 12·7 mg O_2/l., at 10° C about 10·9 mg and at 24° C only 8·3 mg. These figures are for air free from carbon dioxide and containing 20·93 per cent of oxygen. When it is considered that the atmosphere contains 250 mg/l. of oxygen at sea level at 20° C it will be realized that the amount of this vital element available to fish is, at best, much restricted in comparison with the amount available to air-breathing animals.

In stating concentrations of oxygen in water, values in parts per million are usually given, which means milligrammes per litre. Sometimes the concentration is given in percentage of saturation but in this case the temperature must be stated. Water 50 per cent saturated at 10° C, for instance, contains about the same absolute amount of oxygen as water 70 per cent saturated at 28° C. Instead of giving the concentration in p.p.m. the tension of dissolved oxygen in millimetres of mercury may be stated. For water in equilibrium with air at the standard atmospheric pressure of 760 mm of mercury the tension of dissolved oxygen will be about 160 mm. Fry considers that it is always preferable to express the concentration in mg/l[8].

As in mammals, the rate of the respiratory movements in fish bears a general relationship to size, smaller fish making many movements per minute, large fish few. Some fish tend to 'cough' at intervals, ejecting water from the mouth with sudden violence, and it is believed that this tends to rid the gills of foreign matter. As might be expected, fish cough more frequently in turbid water. The regularity of the breathing movements varies very much with different species; some fish generally exhibit a very regular breathing, others, like the stickle-back (*Gasterosteus aculeatus*), tend to be irregular when at rest and 5 to 10 rapid respirations may alternate with pauses lasting several seconds. Irregular and shallow respiration tends to be associated with rest and a good oxygen supply. Van Dam[9] found that in the eel the respiratory movements are very erratic when the animal is resting and that pauses sometimes lasting 5 min occur. Another curious feature of the eel is unilateral ventilation; one side only of the gill apparatus may function, sometimes for hours.

Fish generally react to a deficient oxygen supply by breathing more rapidly and more regularly and by increasing the amplitude of the respiratory movements. The reaction of the stickleback to deoxygenated water is shown in *Figure 5*. Ellis[23] has a similar figure for the perch. Minnows in water deficient in oxygen may breathe up to 300 times per minute. All fish do not react the same way and in some cases the chief symptom is an increase in the depth of breathing, the frequency remaining much the same. Van Dam[9] found that changes in the amplitude of the respiratory movements of the rainbow trout could effect a fourfold increase in the volume of water passed through the branchial chambers whereas an increase in the frequency of breathing only served to raise it 30 per cent. It has been pointed out earlier in this chapter that rapid and laboured respiration appears to be accompanied by a decrease in the utilization—a smaller proportion

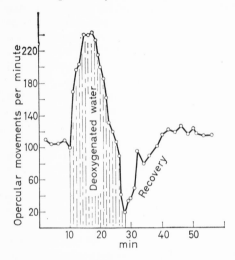

Figure 5. Opercular movement rate for a stickleback in deoxygenated water. At 10 min water boiled for some time and cooled under paraffin was run into the respiration chamber. Aerated water was readmitted at 28 min.

(By courtesy of the *Journal of Experimental Biology*.)

of the oxygen in the water passed is taken up by the blood. When the oxygen supply is deficient the fish therefore has to pass more water through the respiratory apparatus to compensate for this.

Another symptom of respiratory distress is an increased tendency to swim. This may be because the fish senses the unfavourable nature of the environment and tries to find better aerated water, but it is partly due to the fact that forward movement assists the flow of water through the mouth and gill chambers. In some pelagic fish, in fact, forward movement has become essential for life; the mackerel has practically lost the ability to ventilate by the normal method and cannot keep its blood oxygenated when closely confined[24]. The higher the temperature is the more swiftly does dyspnoea develop if the oxygen supply fails. At temperatures near to freezing, the goldfish can survive for long periods in water containing little or no oxygen and appears to be able to perform a considerable amount of anaerobic metabolism[25]. At 3° C trout fry take several minutes to react to water containing only 1·8 mg/l. of oxygen (14 per cent saturation); at 20° C they react immediately with staggering movements and violent gulping (*see* Chapter 3).

The extent to which fish can tolerate low oxygen concentrations has been studied experimentally and estimated from field observations. A considerable literature on the subject has accumulated and at first sight the results do not seem to be in very good agreement. Some of the field studies only provide information about the tolerance to oxygen deficiency at low temperatures as they deal with the survival of fish in frozen lakes and rivers. When the surface of a river or lake is frozen the water is cut off from contact with the air and so one source of oxygen is removed. Light will penetrate clear ice fairly well and some photosynthesis can still go on, but if the ice becomes covered with snow the light is completely cut off, photosynthesis will stop, and there may be a serious degree of oxygen depletion. Thompson[26], who made a study of the death of fish in the Illinois River as a result of freezing, came to the conclusion that dissolved oxygen concentrations below 2 p.p.m. will kill all kinds of fish, and that a variety of species is found only where 4 p.p.m. or more is maintained. Cooper and Washburn[27] (Table 2) made a study of winterkills of fish in southern Michigan lakes in 1944–45. They found that a heavy mortality occurred in those lakes in which the dissolved oxygen concentration fell to 0·6 p.p.m. or less, but no complete kill of fish was encountered. With the pumpkinseeds, chub suckers, bullheads and golden shiners there was a large rate of survival even in lakes where the oxygen was reduced to 0·3 or 0·2 p.p.m., and the blackchin shiners, blacknose shiners and Iowa darters seemed even more resistant. Moyle and Clothier[28] made a study of a prairie lake where snow blanketed the ice in winter and found rather a wide variation in the tolerance to oxygen deficiency shown by the different fish; the largemouth bass appeared to be affected at 2·3 p.p.m. but the bullheads survived at 0·3 p.p.m. Moore[29] studied the survival of lake fish under ice and also their tolerance to different oxygen concentrations at summer temperatures. Moore's work is experimental in nature as many of his observations were made with aquarium fish which were placed in the lake in fish cages. For the winter studies the fish were acclimated to 4° C before being placed in the lake. The data in Table 2 show that the limiting concentrations for different species at low temperatures cover quite a wide range, and in some cases the values for the same fish given by different investigators compare rather badly; see, for example, the figures for pike and yellow perch.

Table 2. Limiting Oxygen Concentrations for Fish at Low Temperatures (0–4° C)*

Fish	p.p.m. *oxygen*	*Ref.*
Blackchin shiner	<0·2	27
Blacknose shiner	<0·2	27
Black bullhead	0·3–1·1	29
Bluegill	0·2–0·4	28
,,	0·6	27
Brown bullhead	0·2–0·3	27
,, ,,	0·3	28
Carp	0·8–1·0	28
Chub sucker	0·3–0·4	27
Crappie	1·4–1·5	29
Golden shiner	0·2–0·3	27
Green sunfish	1·5–3·6	29
Iowa darter	<0·2	27
Largemouth bass	2·3	28
,, ,,	2·3–4·8	29
Orange-spotted sunfish	1·4–4·2	29
Pike	2·3	28
,,	0·3–0·4	27
,,	2·3–3·2	29
Pumpkinseed	0·9–1·4	29
,,	0·3–0·4	27
Rock bass	2·3–3·2	29
White bass	0·2–0·4	28
White sucker	2·0	28
Yellow perch	0·3–0·4	27
,, ,,	1·5–4·8	29

* The data are based mainly on field observations on frozen lakes and rivers. In the case of Reference 29 some of the data are based on experimental work with fish cages.

Moore's winter trials were for 48 h periods. His summer trials, at 15–26° C showed that oxygen concentrations near 5 p.p.m. were well tolerated by all the fish but that concentrations below 3·5 p.p.m. were fatal in less than 24 h to most species. The most extensive ecological investigation is that of Ellis[23] who made 5,809 determinations at 982 stations on rivers and streams of the U.S.A. Ellis found that in the warm season of the year, the waters at 96 per cent of the stations where a good, mixed fish fauna was seen, carried at least 5 p.p.m. of dissolved oxygen. On the basis of his ecological studies Ellis[30] classified freshwater habitats into three categories according to their oxygen content and suitability for fish life: (1) Oxygen 0·3–2·9 p.p.m.; a supply too low for the survival of fish. (2) Oxygen 3·0–4·9 p.p.m.; a supply unfavourably low but tolerated by some species for varying periods. (3) Oxygen 5·0 p.p.m. and upwards; a supply ample and favourable for fish life.

Experimental work to examine the tolerance of fish to low concentrations of dissolved oxygen has gone along two main lines. One basic method is to confine the fish in a fixed volume of water cut off from contact with the air; the oxygen present is gradually used up by the fish which eventually dies, whereupon the concentration of oxygen that remains is measured. This method, which has been in use for 50 years or more, has many defects. In the first place it is obvious that the volume of water used, relative to the size and oxygen demands of the fish, must have a great influence upon the result. If a large fish is confined in a very small volume of water it will reduce the oxygen content to zero or near zero almost at once and then die. If the volume of water is very large the fall in the oxygen content may be so slow that the fish may die from some unrelated cause. Secondly, it is obvious that the concentration at the end of the experiment is not the concentration that the animal can survive, since it has died! Thirdly, the fish is subjected, in an experiment of this kind, not only to a progressive decrease in the supply of oxygen but also to an accumulation of carbon dioxide and changes in the hydrogen ion concentration of the water. The method is more suitable for the study of a related problem—the way the ability of fish to extract oxygen from the water is influenced by the carbon dioxide concentration[31-33]. Nevertheless the 'closed chamber' method still has its supporters and has been used recently to determine lethal oxygen tensions for yellow perch, smallmouth bass and trout[34, 35]. It is argued that the conditions to which fish are subjected in this method resemble those resulting from intermittent discharges of organic oxygen-demanding wastes into polluted streams more closely than those set up by other methods of experiment.

The second basic method is to keep the test fish in running supplies of water in which the oxygen concentration is maintained at selected, fixed values. There are various ways of supplying water of a desired oxygen concentration; apparatus used by Shelford and Fry has been referred to earlier. The method used in experiments carried out at the Water Pollution Research Laboratory at Stevenage is as follows: a supply of unchlorinated borehole water is treated so as to remove the carbon dioxide, and its pH is adjusted as necessary. This water is then set to flow down two vertical columns. A stream of nitrogen is blown up one column so as to produce a supply containing a very low concentration of oxygen. Air is blown up the other to give a supply of well-aerated water. The two supplies are mixed in proportions controlled by a hand-operated valve; by adjusting the two flows as recorded on the flow-meters a mixed supply can be produced containing any desired concentration of oxygen up to saturation level[36]. Davison et al.[37] used a series of columns, one for each desired oxygen concentration. Each was a Pyrex tube 5 ft. high and 2 in. in diameter and was filled with small glass rings up to an overflow near the top. Water ran in at the top of each column at a rate sufficient to keep it full, a small portion going to waste through the overflow. Nitrogen was blown in at the bottom of each tube and bubbling up through the descending water removed some of the oxygen. Control of the nitrogen supply determined the amount of oxygen removed; the treated water went on into 5 or 12 gal. test vessels in which the fish were placed.

Instead of having a water supply of regulated gas content flowing through the test vessel it is possible to control the gas content of the water in small aquaria by blowing in mixtures of oxygen and nitrogen in suitable proportions. Blowing in air will maintain air saturation; a current of nitrogen in sufficient amount and means to keep the water of the aquarium circulating will bring the oxygen content down to near zero. Lindroth [38] used this method for salmon parr in 17 l. aquaria. Alabaster, Herbert and Hemens [39] have studied the survival of rainbow trout and perch at various concentrations of dissolved oxygen and carbon dioxide by placing the fish in aquaria of 40 l. capacity into which mixtures of oxygen, carbon dioxide and nitrogen were blown through ceramic diffusers at 50 ml./sec. Each aquarium was almost filled with water and topped with a glass plate. The small space above the surface of the water became filled with the gas mixture which escaped to waste through a small exhaust vent. Ten trout or ten trout and five perch were used for each experiment and periodic checks were made of the oxygen and carbon dioxide concentrations.

Table 3 gives the limiting oxygen concentrations for a number of fish, as determined experimentally by various workers, using the methods described above. Three general points are evident: there is a reasonably good agreement in the results obtained by different workers studying the same species; secondly, different fish have very different limiting concentrations, thus the requirements of the speckled trout are high, whereas the tench seems to survive near anoxia; thirdly, the figures seem somewhat low compared with those based on field observations at similar temperatures, particularly the 5 p.p.m. standard arrived at by Ellis. This discrepancy is understandable when it is accepted that if fish survive certain adverse conditions for periods of hours or days in the laboratory, it does not follow that they will survive the same conditions in nature indefinitely, feed, grow, reproduce and compete with enemies.

Life for fish, as for other animals, must be something more than the survival of adverse conditions in a state of suspended animation and so

Table 3. Limiting Oxygen Concentrations for Fish*

Fish	Oxygen p.p.m.	Temp. °C	Ref.
Bleak	0·68–1·44	16	48
Blunt-nosed minnow . .	2·25	20–26	49
Brown bullhead . . .	0·3 (est.)	30	42
Brown trout	1·13	6·4	22
,,　,, ...	1·16	9·5–10	,,
,,　,, ...	2·13	18	,,
,,　,, ...	2·8	24	,,
,,　,, ...	1·28–1·6	9·4	34
,,　,, ...	1·64–2·48	17·2	,,
,,　,, ...	2·9	?	47
Carp	1·1	30	,,
Carp (mirror) . . .	0·59–2·5	16	48
Coho salmon	1·3	16	37
,,　,, ...	1·4	20	,,
,,　,, ...	2·0	24	,,
Dace	0·57–1·1	16	48
Eel	<1·0	17	9
Goldfish	0·5	10	42
,, ...	0·6	20	,,
,, ...	0·7	30	,,
Perch	1·1–1·3	16	48
Rainbow trout . . .	2·4–3·7	16	,,
,,　,, . . .	2·5	19–20	50
,,　,, . . .	0·83–1·42	11·1	34
,,　,, . . .	1·05–2·06	18·5	,,
Roach	0·67–0·69	16	48
Salmon parr	2·0–2·2	8	38
Smallmouth bass . . .	0·63–0·98	15·6	34
Speckled trout . . .	2·0	10	42
,,　,, ...	2·2	15	,,
,,　,, ...	2·5	20	,,
,,　,, ...	1·52	3·5	44
,,　,, ...	2·4	23	,,
,,　,, ...	2·5	19–20	50
,,　,, ...	1·35–2·35	15·6	34
Steel-coloured shiner . .	2·25	20–26	49
3-spined stickleback . .	0·25–0·50	?	51
Tench	0·35–0·52	16	48
Yellow perch	2·25	20–26	49
,,　,, ...	0·37–0·88	15·5	35

* The oxygen concentrations given in this table are the minimum values at which the fish named can exist, according to the data in the references cited.   As explained in the text, considerably higher concentrations may be necessary to permit normal or even restricted activity.

the question of how far the activity of fish is controlled by the oxygen concentration of the surrounding water must be examined.   It should be understood that activity does not necessarily mean locomotion and other muscular movement.   All metabolic processes additional to the basic minimum are forms of activity and may demand the expenditure of a considerable amount of energy; the digestion and absorption of food requires the expenditure of energy; as is shown by the observation that the oxygen requirements of unfed fish may be only 50 per cent of the standard, basic value and that of fish fed to repletion may be equal to the 'active' value as determined with the rotating chamber[8].

In 1873 Pflüger expressed the view that the animal cell itself determines its own respiratory exchange and that the oxidations it performs are independent, within wide limits, of the oxygen supplied to it. This view was based almost exclusively on speculative considerations of a teleological character and on the assumption that the oxygen supplied to cells is normally in excess of their requirements.

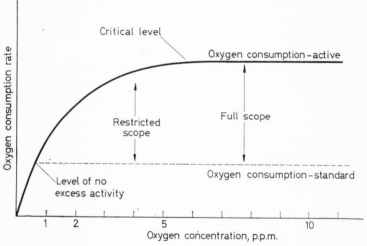

Figure 6. Hypothetical graph to illustrate the principle of respiratory dependence in fish

To some extent Pflüger's hypothesis seems to work with the higher animals; thus it has been shown that the oxygen consumption of man continues at an unchanged rate when the supply is reduced, until the inspired air contains only 12–13 per cent of oxygen, when changes in the respiration rate begin, and similar results have been obtained with dogs and other animals[40]. Fish react in the same way; for many species it has been shown that at any fixed temperature, when the fish is active, the rate of oxygen consumption is independent of the concentration down to a certain critical level (*Figure 6*). Below this critical level the activity of the animal begins to be restricted by lack of oxygen, and is progressively limited with a further fall in the oxygen tension until a point is reached when the fish employing its respiratory

20

apparatus to its utmost capacity is only capable of extracting from the water the amount of oxygen it normally uses when in a state of complete rest. This important oxygen concentration is the 'level of no excess activity' as defined by Fry[41]. Basu[42] has extended the concept to include all combinations of oxygen and carbon dioxide.

At a somewhat lower oxygen concentration the fish will die, and the oxygen tension which is fatal in some selected time convenient for experiment, usually 48 or 96 h, is usually referred to as the 'asphyxial level'. The determination of asphyxial levels must be carried out with an apparatus designed to keep the oxygen concentration constant. The concentration of oxygen remaining when a fish has died in a sealed container is known as the 'residual level' and is usually substantially lower than the asphyxial level because the fish may use up a considerable measure of the oxygen in the process of dying. As pointed out earlier, the value of the residual level will depend on the relative size of the container used; most workers in these experiments have used vessels 10 to 50 times the volume of the fish.

In some species the critical tension—the tension at which the activity begins to be restricted by lack of oxygen—may be well below saturation. At 20° C the goldfish is unaffected down to 34 mm Hg of O_2 and at 5° C the critical tension is as low as 15 mm Hg, less than 10 per cent saturation[15]. Prosser et al.[43] obtained similar results and showed that goldfish could develop some degree of acclimatization to low concentrations of oxygen and that this acclimatization is accompanied by increased red-cell counts. On the other hand Graham[44] found that the critical tension for the speckled trout is as high as 150 mm Hg at 24·5° C which means that the water must be near to air saturation before the fish can display full activity. Job[16], in a very complete study of the metabolism of this fish, has obtained very similar results. Some further data are given in Table 4.

Table 4. Critical Levels of Oxygen*

Fish	Oxygen concentration	Temp. °C	Ref.
Goldfish	2.5 p.p.m.	20	8
Goldeye	9·0 p.p.m.	10	8
,, .	11.0 p.p.m.	15	8
Perch	7·0 p.p.m.	20	8
Speckled trout . . .	6–7 p.p.m.	5	8, 16
,, ,, ...	6–7 p.p.m.	10	8, 16
,, ,, ...	9·0 p.p.m.	20	8, 16
Lake trout (1 y.) . . .	abt. ⅔ saturation	9·5–18	52
,, ,, (2 y.) . . .	abt. ¾ saturation	9·5–18	52

* This table gives the concentrations below which the activity of the fish named begins to be restricted.

21

A moderate degree of oxygen shortage can curtail the activity of fish as measured by their swimming capabilities. Thus the cruising speed of the perch drops slowly as the oxygen concentration is depressed from 8 to 3 p.p.m. at 25° C and at still lower concentrations falls very sharply[8] (*Figure 7*). Largemouth bass can swim against a 0·8 ft./sec current when the water is saturated with oxygen but fail to do so if the supply is reduced to 5 p.p.m. The results obtained with other fish showed some interesting differences. Juvenile chinook and

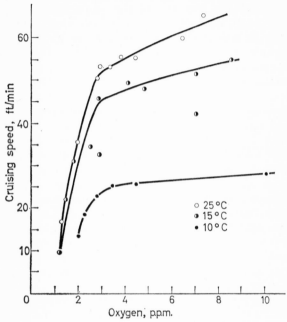

Figure 7. The cruising speed of the yellow perch in relation to temperature and oxygen content

(From Fry[8], by courtesy of Academic Press.)

coho salmon were able to swim continuously against a current of 0·8 ft./sec for one day at oxygen concentrations only slightly higher, by about 1 p.p.m., than those necessary for the survival of quiescent fish. This suggests that these fish have a very high respiratory efficiency[45]. A reduction of activity brought about by oxygen deficiency may involve inability to feed. Thus Davison *et al.*[37] found that coho salmon would survive 2 p.p.m. of oxygen for 30 days but ate sluggishly and lost weight. At 3 p.p.m. they fed as well as controls in well-aerated water.

Oxygen concentrations which will just permit existence for limited periods in the laboratory therefore cannot suffice in nature, but laboratory experiments are useful in that they supply information about the relative resistance of different species, and the extent to which fish can tolerate temporary subjection to oxygen shortage. When some degree of pollution is inevitable the scientist may have to decide on some lower limit below which the oxygen concentration must not drop. At any particular temperature the difference between the oxygen consumption of a fish in full activity and the basic minimum of rest has been termed the 'scope for activity'[8]. The standard suggested for polluted water is 'half scope', meaning half the scope at air saturation[42]. For the speckled trout, for example, this lies a little below 6 p.p.m. oxygen at 10° C. This standard is, of course, quite arbitrary.

In a consideration of the half scope standard Fry[46] has pointed out that though many fish require air saturation for full activity it would be unrealistic to require a minimum standard of oxygen concentration in polluted waters that would permit the full scope of all species. Fry considers Basu's standard to be a useful one but notes that there are practical difficulties involved. The available evidence shows that the problem is complicated, for the scope varies not only with the species of fish concerned but with its size and the temperature. Thus in the speckled trout the scope is about constant from 5 to 20° C for 1,000 g fish but rises with the temperature for smaller ones[16]. Furthermore, there is evidence that oxygen concentrations below the adequate but above the lethal level can cause fish to be restless and to move away from the polluted water to seek a more favourable environment. The concentration at which this effect begins might be termed the 'oxykinetic level'.

In concluding this discussion of the oxygen requirements of fish and the extent to which they may be met or denied, the writer would like to quote from Fry[46]: '. . . it would appear that the best single standard for the oxygen requirements of fish would be some measure similar to the half scope level. The incipient lethal level is in general far too low a level to be an acceptable standard. Moreover, such lethal levels as have been determined have often been obtained by methods which have made them serious underestimates even for the mere support of life.'

REFERENCES

[1] Katz, M. and Gaufin, A. R. The effects of sewage pollution on the fish population of a midwestern stream. *Trans. Amer. Fish. Soc.*, 82 (1952) 156–65

[2] Wiebe, A. H. Biological survey of the upper Mississippi river with special reference to pollution. *Bull. U.S. Bur. Fish.*, 43 (1927) 137–67

[3] Hughes, G. M. and Shelton, G. The mechanism of ventilation in three freshwater teleosts. *J. exp. Biol.*, 35 (1958) 807–23

[4] Von Skramlik, E. Über den Kreislauf bei den Fischen. *Ergebn. Biol.*, 2 (1935) 1–130

[5] Mott, J. C. The cardiovascular system. In *The Physiology of Fishes, Volume 1—Metabolism*, ed. by Margaret E. Brown. 1957. New York; Academic Press

[6] Moussa, T. A. Physiology of the accessory respiratory organs of the teleost *Clarias lazera* (C. & V.). *J. exp. Zool.*, 136 (1957) 419–54

[7] Carter, G. S. and Beadle, L. C. The fauna of the swamps of the Paraguayan Chaco in relation to its environment—II. Respiratory adaptations in the fishes. *J. Linn. Soc. (Zool.)*, 37 (1931) 327–66

[8] Fry, F. E. J. The aquatic respiration of fish. In *The Physiology of Fishes, Volume 1—Metabolism*, ed. by Margaret E. Brown. 1957. New York; Academic Press

[9] Van Dam, L. *On the Utilization of Oxygen and Regulation of Breathing in Some Aquatic Animals*. 1938. Groningen; Drukkerij 'Volharding'

[10] Shelford, V. E. Equipment for maintaining a flow of oxygen-free water, and for controlling gas content. *Bull. Ill. Lab. nat. Hist.*, 11 (1918) 573–5

[11] Fry, F. E. J. A fractionating column to provide water of various dissolved oxygen content. *Canad. J. Technol.*, 29 (1951) 144–6

[12] Jones, J. R. E. The oxygen consumption of *Gasterosteus aculeatus* L. in toxic solutions. *J. exp. Biol.*, 23 (1947) 298–311

[13] Spoor, W. A. A quantitative study of the relationship between the activity and oxygen consumption of the goldfish, and its application to the measurement of respiratory metabolism in fishes. *Biol. Bull., Wood's Hole*, 91 (1946) 312–25

[14] Black, E. C., Fry, F. E. J. and Scott, W. J. Maximum rates of oxygen transport for certain fresh water fishes. *Anat. Rec.*, 75 (1939) Supp. 80

[15] Fry, F. E. J. and Hart, J. S. The relation of temperature to oxygen consumption in the goldfish. *Biol. Bull., Wood's Hole*, 94 (1948) 66–77

[16] Job, S. V. The oxygen consumption of *Salvelinus fontinalis*. *Univ. Toronto Stud. biol.*, No. 61 (1955) 39 pp

[17] Fry, F. E. J. and Hart, J. S. Cruising speed of goldfish in relation to water temperature. *J. Fish. Res. Bd Can.*, 7 (1948) 169–75

[18] Bainbridge, R. Speed and stamina in three fish. *J. exp. Biol.*, 37 (1960) 129–53

[19] Heilbrunn, L. V. *An Outline of General Physiology*, 3rd edition. 1955. Philadelphia and London; Saunders

[20] Wright, S. *Applied Physiology*, 9th edition. 1952. London, New York and Toronto; Oxford Univ. Press

[21] Wells, N. A. The importance of the time element in the determination of the respiratory metabolism of fishes. *Proc. nat. Acad. Sci., Wash.*, 18 (1932) 580–85

[22] Gardner, J. A. Report on the respiratory exchange in freshwater fish with suggestions as to further investigations. *Min. Ag. Fish., Fish. Invest.*, Ser. I. 3 (1926) 1–17

[23] Ellis, M. M. Detection and measurement of stream pollution. *Bull. U.S. Bur. Fish.*, 48 (1937) 365–437

24 Hall, F. G.   The ability of the common mackerel and certain other fishes to remove dissolved oxygen from sea water.   *Amer. J. Physiol.*, 93 (1930) 417–21

25 Blazka, P.   The anaerobic metabolism of fish.   *Physiol. Zool.*, 31 (1958) 117–28

26 Thompson, D. H.   Some observations on the oxygen requirements of fishes in the Illinois River.   *Bull. Ill. Lab. nat. Hist.*, 15 (1925) 423–37

27 Cooper, G. P. and Washburn, G. N.   Relation of dissolved oxygen to winter mortality of fish in Michigan lakes.   *Trans. Amer. Fish. Soc.*, 76 (1949) 23–33

28 Moyle, J. B. and Clothier, W. D.   Effects of management and winter oxygen levels on the fish population of a prairie lake.   *Trans. Amer. Fish. Soc.*, 88 (1958) 178–85

29 Moore, W. G.   Field studies on the oxygen requirements of certain fresh-water fishes.   *Ecology*, 23 (1942) 319–29

30 Ellis, M. M.   Water conditions affecting life in Elephant Butte reservoir.   *Bull. U.S. Bur. Fish.*, 49 (1940) 257–304

31 Fry, F. E. J. and Black, E. C.   The influence of carbon dioxide on the utilization of oxygen by certain species of fish in Algonquin Park, Ontario.   *Anat. Rec.*, 72 (1938) Supp. 47

32 Fry, F. E. J., Black, V. S. and Black, E. C.   Influence of temperature on asphyxiation of young goldfish (*Carassius auratus* L.) under various tensions of oxygen and carbon dioxide.   *Biol. Bull., Wood's Hole*, 92 (1947) 217–24

33 Black, E. C., Fry, F. E. J. and Black, V. S.   The influence of carbon dioxide on the utilization of oxygen by some fresh-water fish.   *Canad. J. Zool.*, 32 (1954) 408–20

34 Burdick, G. E., Lipschuetz, M., Dean, H. J. and Harris, E. J.   Lethal oxygen concentrations for trout and smallmouth bass.   *N.Y. Fish and Game J.*, 1 (1954) 84–97

35 Burdick, G. E., Dean, H. J. and Harris, E. J. Lethal oxygen concentrations for yellow perch. *N.Y. Fish and Game J.*, 4 (1957) 92–101

36 *Water Pollution Research 1955.*   1956.   London; H.M.S.O.

37 Davison, R. C., Breese, W. P., Warren, C. E. and Doudoroff, P.   Experiments on the dissolved oxygen requirements of cold-water fishes.   *Sewage industr. Wastes*, 31 (1959) 950–66

38 Lindroth, A.   Vitality of salmon parr at low oxygen pressure.   *Rep. Inst. Freshw. Res. Drottningholm*, No. 29 (1949) 49–50

39 Alabaster, J. S., Herbert, D. W. M. and Hemens, J.   The survival of rainbow trout (*Salmo gairdnerii* Richardson) and perch (*Perca fluviatilis* L.) at various concentrations of dissolved oxygen and carbon dioxide.   *Ann. appl. Biol.*, 45 (1957) 177–88

40 Krogh, A.   *The Respiratory Exchange of Animals and Man.*   1916.   London; Longmans Green

41 Fry, F. E. J.   Effects of the environment on animal activity.   *Univ. Toronto Stud. biol.*, 55 (1947) 62 pp

42 Basu, S. P.   Active respiration of fish in relation to ambient concentrations of oxygen and carbon dioxide. *J. Fish. Res. Bd Can.*, 16 (1959) 175–212

43 Prosser, C. L., Barr, L. M., Pinc, R. D. and Lauer, C. Y.   Acclimation of goldfish to low concentrations of oxygen.   *Physiol. Zool.*, 30 (1957) 137–41

[44] Graham, J. M.   Some effects of temperature and oxygen pressure on the metabolism of the speckled trout, *Salvelinus fontinalis*.   *Canad. J. Res.*, 27 D (1949) 270–88

[45] Katz, M., Pritchard, A. and Warren, C. E.   Ability of some salmonids and a centrarchid to swim in water of reduced oxygen content. *Trans. Amer. Fish. Soc.*, 88 (1959) 88–95

[46] Fry, F. E. J.   The oxygen requirements of fish.   In *Biological Problems in Water Pollution.   Trans. 1959 Seminar, Robert A. Taft Sanit. Eng. Cent. Tech. Rep. W 60-3, Cincinnati, Ohio, 1960*

[47] Paton, D. N.   Observations on the amount of dissolved oxygen in water required by young salmonidae.   *Proc. roy. Soc. Edinb.*, 24 (1904) 145–50

[48] *Water Pollution Research 1956.*   1957.   London; H.M.S.O.

[49] Wilding, J. L.   The oxygen thresholds for three species of fish.   *Ecology*, 20 (1939) 253–63

[50] Gutsell, J. S.   Influence of certain water conditions, especially dissolved gases, on trout.   *Ecology*, 10 (1929) 77–96

[51] Pruthi, H. S.   Preliminary observations on the relative importance of the various factors responsible for the death of fishes in polluted waters. *J. Mar. biol. Ass. U.K.*, 14 n.s. (1927) 729–39

[52] Gibson, E. S. and Fry, F. E. J.   The performance of the lake trout, *Salvelinus namaycush*, at various levels of temperature and oxygen pressure.   *Canad. J. Zool.*, 32 (1954) 252–60

3

THE REACTIONS OF FISH TO WATER
OF LOW OXYGEN CONCENTRATION

In the previous chapter it is pointed out that fish are 'oxykinetic', that they are made restless by lack of oxygen and stimulated to move away to better aerated water.   If fish have an instinctive ability to detect low concentrations of oxygen they differ from man.   Experiment shows that a man will breathe an atmosphere containing much less than the normal proportion of oxygen with little or no discomfort; when the gas mixture contains less than 13 per cent there is little distress and the subject may become blue and lose consciousness without being aware that there is anything seriously wrong[1].   If a man is set to breathe pure nitrogen, carbon dioxide is eliminated normally and loss of consciousness develops very suddenly and without any warning in about 45 sec[2].

Experimental work on the reactions of fish to varying concentrations of atmospheric gases was begun by Shelford and Allee[3] with the apparatus called the 'gradient tank'.   This is a rectangular tank, about 120 cm long, 15 cm wide and 13 cm deep.   The front wall is of glass, to permit observation of the fish.   Water runs in at both ends of the tank through T-pieces, the cross bars of which contain a number of holes.   Water runs out at the centre of the tank through drain tubes at the top and the bottom.   The outer openings of the drain tubes are placed at such a height that the tank does not empty but remains filled nearly to the top.   If fully aerated water runs in at one end and deoxygenated water runs in at the other an oxygen gradient is set up by the mixing of the two supplies in the middle of the tank. The nature of the gradient can be varied to some extent by altering the rates of flow; thus if both supplies flow fast the zone of mixing may occupy only a small, middle region of the tank; if both supplies flow very gently the gradient may extend from end to end.

In each experiment the apparatus is set working and a fish is liberated in the centre of the tank.   Its behaviour is watched and its movements can be recorded on a narrow, vertical chart.   The width of the chart represents the tank and a time scale is marked off, starting at the top.   Equipped with chart and stop-clock the observer watches the fish and copies its movements by drawing a line on the

27

chart; thus a rapid dash from one end of the tank to the other is represented by a horizontal line at the appropriate point on the time scale. If the fish remains motionless the trace becomes a vertical line on the part of the chart corresponding with the part of the tank where the fish stays. Comments on the animal's behaviour can be written alongside the trace.

Shelford and Allee used about 16 American species of fish in their experiments. They concluded, first, that there appeared to be little or no response to a nitrogen gradient and that the concentration of this gas is of no importance provided that it is not present in such excess as to cause 'gas-bubble disease', and secondly, that fish react

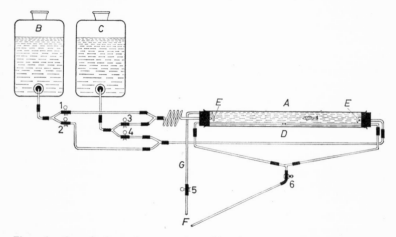

Figure 8. General scheme of apparatus for studying the reactions of fish to water of low oxygen concentration. 1, 2, 3, 4, 5: pinch-clips; 6: screw-clip; E: baffles

negatively to a deficiency of oxygen, indicating their dislike by moving away, rising to the surface, gulping and coughing. The results with the gradient tank, however, do not indicate the concentration of oxygen producing these reactions with any degree of accuracy and the way the reaction is influenced by the temperature of the water was not studied.

A somewhat different type of apparatus designed by the writer[4] is an improvement in that it can present a moving fish with a sharp step of known value in the oxygen concentration. The essential details of the apparatus are shown in *Figure 8*. The fish are confined in a long glass tube, *A*. For sticklebacks, small minnows and trout fry one of 50 cm in length and of 3·4 cm internal diameter is a convenient size.

Aspirator *B* can supply fully aerated water to both ends of the tube or to one end only, as required. Aspirator *C*, similarly, can supply water of a different oxygen concentration. Two outlets *D*, from the centre of the reaction tube, lead to waste at *F*; the screw-clip 6 controls the rate of flow. The air-discharge tube *G* serves for the expulsion of all air from the tube. When the two supplies are running at sufficient speed, one into the left- and the other into the right-hand side of the reaction tube a very sharp, vertical separation is set up at the centre. This can be checked by colouring one supply with dye when the screw-clip 6 can be adjusted to a suitable setting.

An experiment is conducted in the following way. The two water supplies are prepared, their temperature adjusted and the oxygen concentrations checked. A fish is placed in the reaction tube and this is filled with water from aspirator *B*, all bubbles being expelled through *G*. This is important because fish react sharply to bubbles or any other objects inside the tube but take little or no notice of objects outside it. The fully oxygenated water is set running through both halves of the tube; when the fish has become accustomed to its surroundings and is moving normally the chart record can be started. The animal's movements are copied for 2–3 min and then the flow of water on one side is stopped and the water of low oxygen concentration in aspirator *C* is run in instead. If the fish performs exploratory movements and visits both ends of the reaction tube it is best to start the flow of poorly oxygenated water in the half of the tube from which the fish is absent; if the fish is sluggish, as is usually the case at low temperatures, it is necessary to admit the new supply on the side in which the fish has elected to stay. The way the movements of the fish are recorded on the charts will be readily understood on examining the following text-figures. If a changeover of the two supplies is made the fully aerated water is run through both halves of the reaction tube before the supply deficient in oxygen is set flowing in the new direction.

Some typical records for sticklebacks, at 13° C, are set out in *Figure 9*. Their reactions to oxygen concentrations below 3 p.p.m.—at this temperature about 28 per cent saturation—conform to a fairly definite pattern. The fish has no immediate appreciation of the low oxygen concentration and generally swims across the boundary without any hesitation. Occasionally it will make a sudden, jerky respiratory movement but swims on. In a series of 15 experiments at 13° C with oxygen concentrations up to 3 p.p.m. the various fish crossed the tube centre without hesitation about 92 times; the record for 0·8 p.p.m. shows five such traverses at 8–10 min. If the animal remains in the low-oxygen zone for any length of time a dyspnoea develops, the amplitude and frequency of the respiratory movements increasing; at the same time random movement seems to be incited and the fish may struggle (*see* the record for 0·26 p.p.m. at 5 min and 14 min). Sooner or later this random movement takes the animal across the boundary into the well-aerated water when the stimulus to swimming seems to disappear. Usually this happens with the greatest abruptness so that the fish only swims about 10 cm into the well-aerated water and then becomes motionless for a minute or two while its respiratory movements return to normal. Thus it appears to

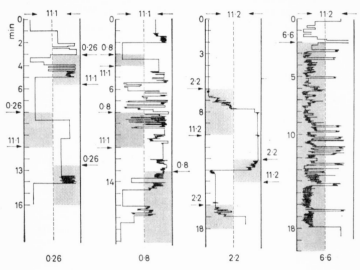

Figure 9. The reactions of sticklebacks to water containing 0·26, 0·8, 2·2 *and* 6·6 p.p.m. *of oxygen (temperature* 13° C). *The figures at the arrows indicate the oxygen concentration; thus the first experiment was begun with water containing* 11·1 p.p.m. *flowing through both halves of the tube; water containing* 0·26 p.p.m. *was run in on the right at* 3 min

(By courtesy of the *Journal of Experimental Biology.*)

select the high-oxygen zone, but the basis of this selection is simply the sudden removal of the stimulus to swimming. If the poorly oxygenated water is run through both halves of the tube a stickleback will keep up continual exploratory movement, becoming more and more agitated; when well-aerated water is admitted on one side the fish stops moving immediately it comes in contact with this and remains still until it has recovered.

When the oxygen concentration tested is 3–5 p.p.m. the results are more variable. Respiratory distress, agitated swimming, apparent recognition of the well-aerated water, rest and recovery generally form the behaviour pattern, the dyspnoea taking a little longer to develop. Occasionally, however, the fish does not leave the poorly oxygenated water and does not struggle very much; by increasing the amplitude and frequency of its breathing movements it seems to succeed in obtaining enough oxygen for its needs. The fourth record in *Figure 9* is for water containing 6·6 p.p.m. oxygen; in this case the stickleback seemed to have a preference for the left side of the tube and although it made several visits to the fully aerated water it persisted in returning.

Some further records for the stickleback at 13° C are given in *Figure 10*. In these experiments it was possible to make counts of the

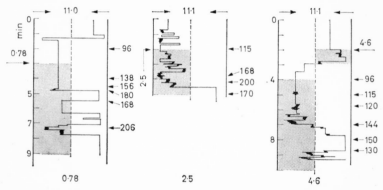

Figure 10. Further records of the reactions of sticklebacks to water of low oxygen concentration at 13° C. The figures on the right of each chart give the number of opercular movements per minute

(By courtesy of the *Journal of Experimental Biology*.)

respiratory movements and these are given on the right of each chart. The centre record shows very clearly how the respiration rate speeds up in the poorly oxygenated water and how recovery begins when the fish crosses over to the right-hand side and stops still. In the third record it will be noted that the fish re-entered the low-oxygen zone at 8–9 min before it had recovered completely.

The results of 32 experiments with *Gasterosteus* at 13° C are summarized in *Figure 11*. Here the horizontal scale gives the oxygen concentration of the 'low' zone; in every case fully aerated water is presented as the alternative. The ordinates are the 'reaction times', the times the fish took to leave the poorly oxygenated water. In some cases they swam into this of their own volition, in others it was admitted to the half of the tube in which they had taken up a position. The reaction times are, of course, very approximate, and in some cases it was obvious that the fish were trying desperately to find their way out of the low-oxygen zone but could not hit on the right direction.

At low temperatures the stickleback exhibits a generally similar reaction to water of low oxygen concentration but the whole performance is in slow motion. *Figure 12* shows three records for fish that had been gradually cooled down from 13° C to 3° C over a period of 9–10 h and were then tested with water of this temperature containing 0·3, 1·1 and 3·5 p.p.m. of oxygen. A description of the

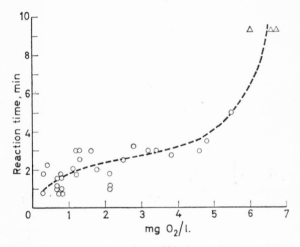

Figure 11. Reaction times for sticklebacks at 13° C. *Triangle points indicate concentrations of oxygen at which no definite result was obtained*

(By courtesy of the *Journal of Experimental Biology*.)

first experiment will be sufficient. Before the low-oxygen water is admitted the fish rests motionless on the bottom of the reaction tube, breathes slowly, regularly and almost imperceptibly and appears to be asleep. On running in the 0·3 p.p.m. water it does not move but soon the respiration rate begins to rise. At 6 min the respiratory movements speed up to 90 per min and become heaving and of great amplitude. The fish begins turning its eyes about and seems to wake up; suddenly it begins to swim, it crosses the boundary zone and almost immediately rests again upon the bottom, its respirations returning to the original frequency and amplitude. At 10 min the poorly oxygenated water is run in on the right-hand side and the same performance is seen, the reaction taking about 4 min. In the 1·1 p.p.m. experiment it will be seen that the development of dyspnoea is much slower, the reaction taking about 11 min, and when the fish is eventually stimulated to swim it moves very lazily. At 3·5 p.p.m. the fish is motionless with no sign of respiratory distress at the end of the experiment.

At this low temperature the response is slow because the development of respiratory distress takes such a time. At 20° C, when a

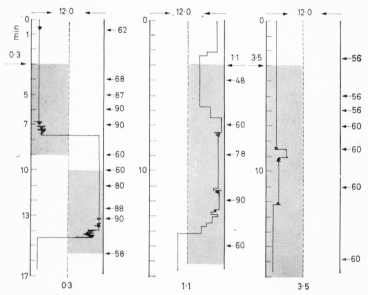

Figure 12. The reactions of sticklebacks to water of low oxygen concentration at 3° C. The figures on the right of each chart give the number of opercular movements per minute

(By courtesy of the *Journal of Experimental Biology*.)

stickleback meets water of very low oxygen concentration respiratory difficulties appear almost immediately so that the fish appears violently irritated and retreats at once. The reaction fails occasionally when the boundary is crossed in a wild rush but the fish then struggles frantically until it has found its way back.

The behaviour of minnows in the same apparatus is essentially similar to that described for *Gasterosteus* but is less dependent on the temperature. Even at 3° C when the fish enters water of low oxygen concentration a severe dyspnoea develops quite quickly, and with gulping respiratory movements of great amplitude the fish returns to

2 +

the well-aerated water. At 24° C the reaction is extremely sharp and minnows promptly avoid water containing 4 p.p.m. of oxygen; attempts to enter it quickly induce great distress with an opercular movement rate of 4–5 per sec.

Trout fry prove very good subjects for experiment with this apparatus and behave somewhat better than minnows. Minnows are apt to be very nervous and sometimes swim very erratically, especially if they are not fully acclimated to the temperature at which the experiment is run. Four typical records for the trout fry are given

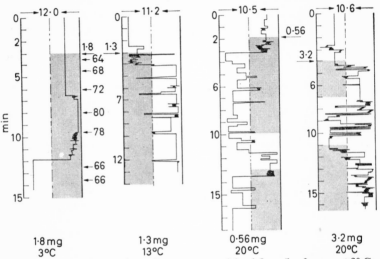

Figure 13.   The reactions of trout fry to water containing 1·8 mg/l. of oxygen at 3° C; 1·3 mg/l. at 13° C; 0·56 and 3·2 mg/l. at 20° C.   The figures opposite the large arrows indicate the oxygen content of the water running into the experiment tube.   Figures opposite the small arrows are counts of the opercular movements (number per minute)

(By courtesy of the *Journal of Experimental Biology*.)

in *Figure 13*.   At 3° C, as with the stickleback, the response takes some time to develop.   At first the fish breathes very regularly and quietly and appears to be asleep, but the respiratory movements gradually quicken and become deeper while the fish begins turning its eyes about, and raises itself on its pectoral fins with its body arched in a curious posture, the dorsal muscles contracted and the snout pointing upwards. Eventually it begins to swim in an uneasy fashion and on crossing to the well-aerated water 'falls asleep' again.   At 13° C the response is much more prompt, visits to the poorly oxygenated water provoke a dyspnoea in 5–7 sec and a quick return.   The 1·3 mg (1·3 p.p.m.)

record in *Figure 13* is interesting; it shows that the trout made several return visits to the left half of the tube after being driven from it, and that the depth to which it penetrated the low-oxygen zone became progressively reduced. At 20° C the response to a concentration of 0·56 p.p.m. is extremely sharp, the trout stagger, gulp violently and retreat in less than 5 sec and a concentration of 3·2 p.p.m. also gives a very good avoiding reaction.

It has been stated that fish have never been seen killed outright by sewage-polluted water unless they are trapped and cannot get away[5], and Thompson[6], discussing the reactions of fish to oxygen deficiency in the Illinois River, attributes to them an ability to avoid oxygen concentrations that would be fatal. The general conclusions to be drawn from the experiments with sticklebacks, minnows and trout that have just been described, is that fish do not have an innate, instinctive ability to recognize water of abnormally low oxygen tension, that they will swim into it, or remain in it should it flow over them, provided that immediate respiratory distress does not develop, and that very low oxygen concentrations and exacting oxygen requirements can, however, induce respiratory distress so quickly that a very prompt rejection can be displayed.

Earlier in this chapter it is stated that man can succumb to a diminished oxygen supply very suddenly, apparently without being aware that anything is wrong. Nothing like this has been seen by the writer in his experiments with fish; in some cases the fish would enter water very deficient in oxygen and extreme respiratory distress would come on but the fish would always continue to swim. Even when they lost their sense of balance they would keep up movement and on finding their way into the well-aerated water they would recover very quickly. The rate at which dyspnoea develops appears to be the essential factor in deciding whether fish will enter water of a lower oxygen concentration, and here the temperature is of great importance. One example can serve to illustrate this: at 3° C water containing only 0·5 p.p.m. of oxygen will be tolerated by the stickleback for over 5 min; at 20° C the same concentration will provoke respiratory distress in under 5 sec.

Another apparatus which has been used to test the reactions of fish to oxygen deficiency is the 'channelled avoidance trough'. This was devised by Jones *et al.*[7] to test the reactions of salmon and trout to pulp-mill effluents, and it was used later in a slightly modified form by Whitmore, Warren and Doudoroff[8] for the study of the extent to which salmon, largemouth bass and bluegills would avoid water of low oxygen concentration. The complete apparatus, with its series of fractionating columns, is somewhat complicated but its principle is simple and is explained by *Figure 14.* The trough has a large main compartment *a*, in which the fish may move about freely, and into this main compartment open four channels, *b*, *c*, *d* and *e*, formed by the insertion of three parallel glass partitions. At the end of the trough four inlet tubes discharge water into the channels; two of these, *c* and *e*, discharge fully aerated water like that in the main compartment; the other two discharge water of reduced oxygen content. All four supplies flow down the channels as indicated by the arrows and out through slot drains located where the channels open into the main compartment of the tank. The slot openings of the drains are placed a little above the floor of the trough and the fish are guided over them by a sloping baffle. Fully aerated water runs in at the opposite ends of the apparatus to meet the supplies coming down the channels and

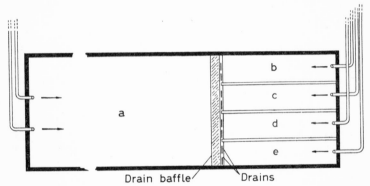

Figure 14. The principle of the 'channelled avoidance trough'

to pass out by the same drains. Experiments with dye showed a sharp boundary between the water coming down the channels and that in the main compartment.

The tank measures 112 in. long by 24 in. wide by 12 in. deep, with channels 36 in. long. The depth of water is $4\frac{1}{2}$ in. Fish of fair size can be tested; the salmon used by Whitmore and colleagues were up to 110 mm long, the largemouth bass a little smaller. The experiments were carried out in the following way: 10 to 35 fish are placed in the tank and when they have begun to move about freely observations are begun and are continued for 45 min. In the earlier study with pulp-mill effluents the number of times the different channels were entered was counted and the 'per cent avoidance' computed by the formula $100(E-A)/E$, where A is the total number of entries of all fish into channels containing effluent (*b* and *d*), and E is the total number of entries into the control channels (*c* and *e*). This formula is based on the assumption that the number of entries into the two effluent channels would be approximately the same as the number of entries into the control channels had there been no avoidance of, nor preference for, those containing the effluent. It will be seen that under these circumstances the formula gives a percentage avoidance of zero; a complete rejection of the effluent gives a score of 100.

In the later study with water of low oxygen concentration a new formula for the percentage avoidance is used. It is pointed out that the formula $100(E-A)/E$ has a disadvantage, in that while the percentage avoidance has a maximum value of 100 when the fish demonstrate a complete preference for the control channels, the result given by the formula when the fish enter the test channels more frequently than the control channels can be a negative figure of anything up to infinity. Accordingly the formula $100(M-A)/M$ is used, where M is the sum of entries for *all* channels divided by 2, and A is the sum of entries for the test channels. Using this formula a complete rejection of the effluent again gives a score of 100 per cent and a complete rejection of the control conditions gives a score of −100. It will be noted that the formulae do not give the same result when a partial avoidance is displayed; thus if in an experiment the fish enter the low-oxygen channels 20 times and the control channels 40 times, the percentage avoidance is 50 by the first formula and 33·3 by the second.

The results obtained with chinook salmon, coho salmon and largemouth bass are shown in *Figure 15*. It will be seen that all three species avoided low concentrations of oxygen, the degree of avoidance increasing as the oxygen concentration is reduced. The coho salmon showed some degree of avoidance at 5·9 p.p.m. O_2, a level which Whitmore and colleagues consider would not produce any respiratory distress. Bluegills were also tested but gave somewhat irregular results.

There is scope for further work on the reactions of fish to oxygen deficiency. Wiebe *et al.*[9], in experiments on the effect of changes in the hydrogen ion concentration on the ability of fish to extract oxygen, in 'closed chamber' conditions, found that all the species tested showed violent motor activity preceding death in highly alkaline water, whereas in strongly acid water this behaviour was not observed. It should be interesting to see how fish behave in the reaction tube or the channelled avoidance trough when presented with water deficient in oxygen and abnormally acid or alkaline. In polluted waters fish may encounter a deficiency of oxygen accompanied by an abnormal amount of carbon dioxide and, perhaps, a series of noxious substances so that the problem is complex. In later chapters dealing with the effects of effluents of different types the effects of oxygen deficiency are discussed further.

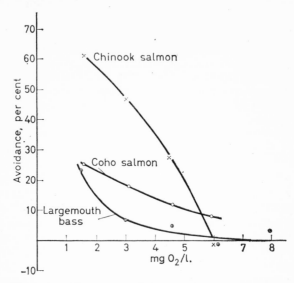

Figure 15. The reactions of chinook salmon, coho salmon and largemouth bass to water of various oxygen concentrations.

(Drawn from the data of Whitmore, Warren and Doudoroff[8].)

REFERENCES

[1] Evans, L.   Starling's *Principles of Human Physiology*.   1949.   10th edn, London; Churchill

[2] Wright, S.   *Applied Physiology*.   1952.   9th edn, London, New York and Toronto; Oxford Univ. Press

[3] Shelford, V. E. and Allee, W. C. The reactions of fishes to gradients of dissolved atmospheric gases. *J. exp. Zool.*, 14 (1913) 207–66

[4] Jones, J. R. E.   The reactions of fish to water of low oxygen concentration. *J. exp. Biol.*, 29 (1952) 403–15

[5] Forbes, S. A.   The effects of stream pollution on fishes and their food. *Nat. Hist. Circ. Ill. geol. Surv.* (1926) 13 pp.

[6] Thompson, D. H.   Some observations on the oxygen requirements of fishes in the Illinois River.   *Bull. Ill. Lab. nat. Hist.*, 15 (1925) 423–37

[7] Jones, B. F., Warren, C. E., Bond, C. E. and Doudoroff, P.   Avoidance reactions of salmonid fishes to pulp-mill effluents. *Sewage industr. Wastes*, 28 (1956) 1403–13

[8] Whitmore, C. M., Warren, C. E. and Doudoroff, P.   Avoidance reactions of salmonid and centrarchid fishes to low oxygen concentrations. *Trans. Amer. Fish. Soc.*, 89 (1960) 17–26

[9] Wiebe, A. H., McGavock, A. M., Fuller, A. C. and Markus, H. C.   The ability of fresh-water fish to extract oxygen at different hydrogen ion concentrations. *Physiol. Zool.*, 7 (1934) 435–48

4

THE MEASUREMENT OF TOXICITY

THE number of substances which may be described as 'poisonous' must be very large and they vary enormously in their power of effect. For man and other air-breathing animals the threshold dose of a poison generally means the maximum quantity that can be taken without causing death. The position of a fish or other aquatic animal living in water containing a toxic substance is somewhat different; instead of receiving by mouth or injection a certain absolute quantity of this substance it is continuously exposed to a certain concentration of the poison, and its condition resembles that of a man regularly drinking water containing lead or constantly breathing air containing some noxious gas or vapour. Therefore it is not surprising that the student of pollution problems directs his attention on the concentration of the substance he is studying, and the way the effect on the fish is related to this rather than on the absolute dose required to harm or kill. Animals have the power to eliminate poisons, at least in some degree, or to destroy them, and whether they can do this sufficiently fast to survive must depend on the concentration of toxic substance to which they are exposed.

In testing the effect of an effluent or any solution of some particular substance toxic to fish four criteria have been employed to express the time-effect relationship[1]:

(1) The immersion time apparently necessary to initiate the toxic process. This is the time that passes before the first indications of poisoning are evident. Different toxic substances may behave very differently in this respect; with hydrogen cyanide a change in breathing rate is almost immediate but with dilute solutions of ammonia no reaction may be apparent for some considerable time. Poisons acting by way of the gut are probably the slowest in the production of first effects.

(2) The time taken for the toxic process to advance to some well-marked stage; for example, in the case of a substance depressing the rate of oxygen consumption the experiment might aim at determining the time necessary to depress the rate to some critical fraction of the normal. In a great deal of pollution research the time at which the fish lose their sense of balance and float on their sides or upside-down has been used as a criterion to a considerable extent. Wuhrmann[1]

calls this the 'manifestation time', a term which would apply better to criterion (1), just described. He points out that at this stage, if the water in the test vessel is stirred, the fish are not able to oppose the movement of the water but move passively with it. In this condition, therefore, the fish could not escape from a zone of pollution and the criterion is a good one for pollution in running water. In Great Britain and the U.S.A. this criterion is usually known as the 'overturning time'; its adoption has certain advantages in that most of the fish, depending on the toxic substance tested, recover on restoration to fresh water and can be returned to the river or used again. In the latter case care must be taken to ensure that fish used for more than one test preserve their normal degree of resistance; they may become acclimatized to the toxic substance used or they may be permanently harmed or weakened by the experiment. The overturning time is not a completely satisfactory criterion for general use as the nature of the toxic action of the poison influences the result very considerably. Substances which have a marked effect on the nervous system of the animal may induce overturning very early, though the fish may not be killed for a considerable time. Thus minnows will lose their sense of balance in a 40 p.p.m. solution of ortho-cresol but are still alive in 5 h. The overturning time is a satisfactory criterion for comparative study of substances of generally similar physiological effect. In some cases very large numbers of fish have to be used as individual variation in resistance may be considerable (*see Figure 16*).

(3) The minimum time of exposure necessary to carry the toxic process so far that recovery is no longer possible. An effluent can be tested by placing a number of fish in it and removing these, either singly or in batches, to separate vessels of fresh water at suitable time intervals. After sufficient time the fish are examined to see which have recovered and which have died. Experiments on these lines necessitate more work and more animals; Wuhrmann considers the criterion to be one difficult to apply and of little importance. Nevertheless it would seem that experiments on these lines may be valuable if we are dealing with an intermittent pollution following a regular cycle.

(4) The time of immersion necessary to kill the fish. Death is usually assumed to have taken place when the animal ceases breathing or no longer moves after mechanical stimulation. Wuhrmann considers this criterion to be very unsatisfactory and it is true that in some cases the death point may be ill-defined as the fish may linger for long periods in something like deep anaesthesia. The time taken to kill the fish is usually referred to as the 'survival time' but many authors seem to use this term for the time taken to bring about overturning.

For reliable and comparative results the conditions of experiment should be carefully controlled. The recommendations that follow are based, in the main, upon those of Doudoroff *et al.* [2].

(1) The test fish should be a species withstanding captivity well; all the fish used in any one test or series of tests should be of the same species, accurately identified to its correct scientific name and obtained from the same body of water. A strict size limit should be observed, the largest specimens being not more than $1\frac{1}{2}$ times the length of the smallest. The fish should be acclimatized to the temperature at which the tests are made and not fed for two days before use. They should

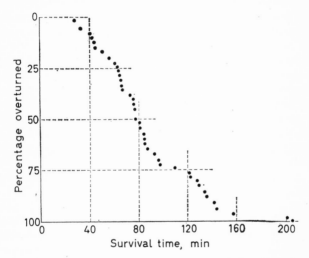

Figure 16. Survival time of rainbow trout in a solution of potassium cyanide containing 0.14 *p.p.m. CN (temperature* $17.5°$ *C)*

(After Herbert and Merkens[6], by courtesy of the *Journal of Experimental Biology*.)

not be collected from a stream in which occurs the type of pollution being studied; a long-standing, mild degree of pollution may have brought about some measure of acclimatization.

A fair variety of fish has been used for experimental pollution studies. The goldfish, used extensively by earlier workers, is now much less popular. Its resistance to adverse conditions, oxygen deficiency in particular, make it an easy type to keep in the laboratory but this same characteristic makes it unsuitable for use as a standard type as tolerance values determined for this species may be very much higher than those for more sensitive types. Minnows (*Phoxinus phoxinus*) have been used extensively in European work. They are conveniently small and as they live in the river in shoals it is easy to obtain large numbers of the same size and physiological condition. They are very sensitive to oxygen deficiency and other adverse conditions, and are liable to attack by a parasite which affects their sense of balance. Sticklebacks (*Gasterosteus aculeatus* and *Pygosteus pungitius*) are another useful small type of fish, very convenient for experiment. They are of a moderate degree of sensitivity and are easily kept in the laboratory. Roberts and Jee[3], in an early discussion of the relative merits of various fish for bio-assay work, did not consider the trout to be a suitable type; they maintained that owing to the fact that it rests on the bottom 'seal fashion', supported by its pectoral fins, and that these may sometimes maintain it in this position even up to and after the point of death, it is difficult to judge the exact time at which loss of equilibrium is produced. They considered perch and roach to be much better types; minnows and sticklebacks were said to be 'inconveniently small'. Experience does not seem to have confirmed these impressions for the rainbow trout is a very popular test fish in Britain, Europe and America, while little use is now made of roach and perch. Popular American types are the bluegill, the fathead minnow, the largemouth bass, the guppy and the channel cat; fingerling chinook and coho salmon are also used.

(2) The water used for making up the solutions should be carefully chosen. Fish should not be tested in a solution made up with water of a type in which they do not normally live. Unpolluted water should be taken, if possible, from the stream in which occurs the type of pollution being studied. Distilled water, particularly that prepared in metal stills, should be avoided. Many tap waters are heavily chlorinated and chlorine is highly toxic to fish. If tap water has to be used it should be tested for possible toxic action at frequent intervals as the amount of chlorine present may vary from time to time. In any experiments with dilute solutions care must be taken to avoid the use of vessels which may be contaminated with traces of chemicals used in a previous test. Davis and Hardcastle[4], in a recent study of the toxicity of herbicides, have described a very good method for overcoming this difficulty. They used large cardboard aquaria fitted with pinhole-free polyethylene liners, each of which was used twice only, inside out for the second test. The cardboard cartons had 'windows' for observation of the fish.

(3) It may be necessary to adopt a standardization for the test temperatures, test containers, depth of liquid, dissolved oxygen and the duration of the tests. Protracted experiments may necessitate the feeding of the animals; this can be done just before the solutions are changed. Wuhrmann and Woker[5] have stressed the desirability of

using large numbers of experimental animals and consider that the minimum number of fish used in any one experiment should not be less than five, and preferably at least 10.

(4) When the concentration of the test solution is low, care must be taken to ensure that the absolute quantity of the toxic substance present is adequate. If the amount that is used up in the toxic process is any considerable proportion of the amount available it is obvious that the concentration to which the fish is exposed will be changed during the experiment and the survival time will be protracted. There are two ways in which errors due to this cause may be avoided. When the fish are placed in fixed volumes of solution the weaker solutions can be made up in larger quantities to balance the fall in concentration and keep the absolute quantity of lethal substance available to the fish constant. For example, in a series of tests 2 l. of solution may be known to be adequate at 10 p.p.m.; for experiments at 5, 3, 2 and 1 p.p.m. the volumes used are 4, 7, 10 and 20 l. Alternatively, the fish can be placed in a container through which passes a running supply of solution. This does not necessitate the making up of very large quantities of solution in the usual way as it is an easy matter to arrange apparatus for making up a test solution automatically. A simple arrangement is shown in *Figure 17*. The vessel *A* with input and overflow supplies water at a constant rate into the funnel *B* of a mixing vessel. Into the funnel concentrated solution drips from the aspirator bottle *C* through a delivery tube drawn out into a fine nozzle. The rate of the drip supply can be controlled roughly by adjusting the length of the capillary portion of the delivery tube, and a number of these tubes, of different length, can be prepared. As the air intake of *C* is at the lower end of the tube *D*, and air has to be sucked in when the level of concentrated solution is high, this will drip at a constant rate. Samples for concentration checks can be drawn off through *E*. Knowing the ratio of the rates of flow—1:100 is very convenient—it is a simple matter to provide a solution of any desired concentration. Some substances may prove difficult on account of limited solubility. More elaborate apparatus is described in the literature; see, for example, that described by Herbert and Merkens[6] and one devised for work on oysters by Collier and Ray[7]. Apparatus now used by the Ministry of Agriculture, Fisheries and Food is shown in the frontispiece. The question arises of the speed at which the dilute solution should flow into the test vessel. It has been stated in Chapter 2 that a fish can take up 80 per cent of the oxygen in the water that passes through its gill chambers; whether a fish can absorb toxic substances from the water to the same extent is not known, but it would appear that when we are working with solutions

of extreme dilution the rate of supply should be at least equal to the total ventilation of the fish in the test vessel.

Herbert and Merkens[6], in their paper on the toxicity of potassium cyanide to trout, have supplied data which serve very well to illustrate some of the points discussed above. They found that the mean survival time in a 0·15 p.p.m. CN solution changed from 28·81 min to 50·80 min when the period of retention in the acclimatization tank was increased from 24 to 191 h. Using fish taken from the same pond they found that when they were graded for size, and tested for survival

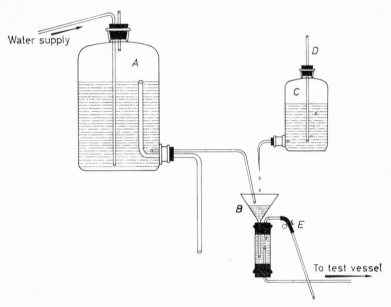

Water supply

Figure 17. Apparatus for making up a supply of dilute solution automatically

time at 0·16 p.p.m. CN, a distinct relationship was evident between size and resistance. The smallest fish (about 6 cm) had a mean survival time of 39 min, the largest (about 17 cm) survived only 16 min. The constant flow apparatus supplied solution at 120 l./h to test vessels containing 31–47 fish.

When a number of fish are placed in a series of solutions of a toxic substance covering a range of concentrations the killing times or overturning times observed bear a relation to the concentration which can be expressed graphically as a 'survival curve'. One of the first survival curves to be published is that determined for the water-flea,

Daphnia, by Warren[8], using solutions of sodium chloride. Warren found that the curve was very nearly a rectangular hyperbola. Powers[9], after an extensive series of experiments with the goldfish, using a variety of salts, acids, drugs and other substances, concluded that for every toxic substance, over a certain range of concentration values, the survival time is inversely related to the concentration. This means that if a graph is drawn in which concentrations are plotted as abscissae and reciprocals of the survival times are plotted as ordinates the points approximate to a straight line (*Figure 18*). This line cuts the concentration axis at a point which Powers called the 'theoretical threshold of toxicity'. The relation between concentration and survival time for the linear portion of the graph can be expressed by the equation $(c-a)t=K$, where c is the concentration, a is the theoretical threshold, t is the survival time and K is a constant

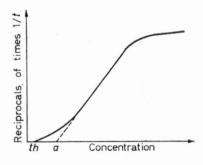

Figure 18. The relation between toxicity, expressed as the reciprocal of the survival time, and concentration, according to Powers[9]. th is the true, and a is the theoretical, threshold of toxicity

characteristic of the substance employed. At high concentrations in Powers' experiments the observed times are longer than the times given by the straight line and at low concentrations the survival times are shorter than the equation demands. As a result the complete concentration–survival time reciprocal graph or 'fatality curve' is sigmoid. Powers seems to have concluded that the fatality curve for all toxic substances should take this sigmoid form, but an examination of his figures for a number of the substances tested (particularly those for caffeine, phenol, pyridine, sodium nitrate and magnesium chloride) raises doubts as to whether the interpolation of the results is satisfactory.

As the concentration falls, in survival time experiments, the survival time increases until a point is reached where it becomes indefinitely long; this is the true 'threshold'. This appears to be a stage of equilibrium; the toxic substance has a speed of operation which diminishes with dilution, and at the threshold the organism holds its own.

Experiments with high concentrations may indicate a 'threshold reaction time'; a stage may be reached when further increase in the concentration will not materially shorten the survival time. The value of this threshold reaction time will depend on the mode of action of the toxic substance. At normal temperatures a small trout or stickleback will live for 15 to 20 min in completely deoxygenated water; therefore a toxic substance whose sole action is the prevention of oxygen intake by the gills cannot kill the fish in less time, however much the concentration is increased. A respiratory depressant, like hydrogen cyanide, which can stop respiration in all the tissues of the animal's body, is only limited in its speed of action by the time it takes to get into the blood and circulate to the vital organs—this may take less than a minute. In some cases a sharp upper limit to the survival curve may be imposed by limited solubility.

Instead of plotting survival curves with linear time and concentration scales logarithmic graph paper may be used to plot the logarithms of the survival times or overturning times against the logarithms of the concentrations. This scheme has certain very great advantages; it enables very wide ranges of concentration and time to be covered without undue crowding of the points. Furthermore it tends to straighten the curve, simplifying the interpolation, and when the survival time and concentration are inversely related the points follow a straight line. Herbert and Merkens[6] give a log/log graph for rainbow trout in potassium cyanide solutions which is linear over the concentration range 0·25–0·07 p.p.m. CN (*Figure 19*). At each concentration at least 30 fish were used and the survival times plotted are the geometric means: survival time $=$ antilog$(\sum \log T)/N$, where T is the survival time of each fish, and N is the number of fish in the test. Over this concentration range, therefore, the concentration/time relationship conforms to the equation $C^n T = k$. At high concentrations, above 0·25 p.p.m., the relationship fails, the survival times are longer than they should be to answer the equation. The survival time, however, is now of the order of 2–5 min and the time taken for the cyanide to get into the bloodstream may be an important factor. An extrapolation of the linear portion of the graph gives a survival time of 0·5 sec at 1 p.p.m. CN, which is hardly possible.

Burdick[10] considers that the log/log graph can be improved by the application of two corrections. He points out that concentration can affect time only in that range lying between the concentration producing a minimum time for death and the threshold value for concentration when the survival time becomes indefinite. The general equation for the survival curve therefore becomes $(C-a)^n (T-b) = K$, where a is the threshold concentration and b is the threshold reaction time. The general form of log/log survival curves corresponding to equations of this type is shown in *Figure 20*. Wuhrmann[1] also considers that this equation, which he says is well known in pharmacology, is the best general expression for the toxicity/concentration relationship. Hynes[11] considers this equation to be a refinement only. Herbert and Downing[12] have pointed out that the equation predicts that when the concentration of poison equals the threshold concentra-

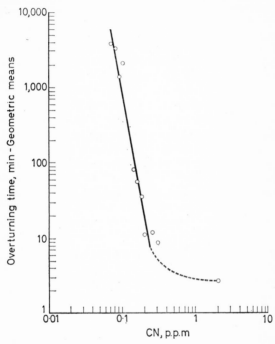

Figure 19. Survival curve for rainbow trout in potassium cyanide solutions at 17·5° C

(Drawn from the data of Herbert and Merkens[6].)

tion an infinite time will elapse before symptoms of poisoning become manifest. It is only fair to point out that the equation $C^n T = k$ also predicts an infinite survival time when the concentration of the toxic substance is zero. Furthermore, it admits no threshold concentration and no threshold reaction time. Nevertheless this equation is reasonably applicable in cases where the threshold concentration is very low and the threshold reaction time is very short. Lloyd's survival-time data[13] for the trout in zinc sulphate solutions made up with soft water interpolate as a straight line and so do some of the writer's results with sticklebacks (*Figure 21*). Lloyd's graphs for solutions made up with hard water are curvilinear. Wuhrmann's data[1] for cyanide, ammonia and phenol plot as curves; Grindley's results[14] for sodium arsenite, sodium arsenate and sodium picrate give straight lines. Even when the results available do give a straight-line graph it may not be safe to assume that the relationship holds at untried dilutions, and estimates of toxicity based on extrapolation may be unreliable.

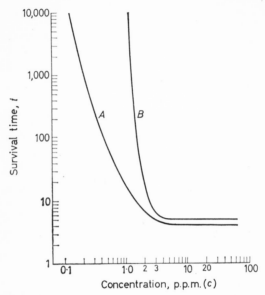

Figure 20. Hypothetical survival curves conforming to the equation of Wuhrmann[1] and Burdick[10]. The equation to curve A is $(C-0.1)^2(T-4)=10$ and that to curve B is $(C-1)^3(T-5)=10$

One cannot assume with safety that the survival time will continue to lengthen with dilution, let alone how fast it will do so. The writer has shown that over the concentration range 0·4–0·0015 N the toxicity of copper nitrate to toad tadpoles *increases* with dilution. At lower concentrations the survival time lengthens again so that at about 0·0003 N it returns to the value it has at 0·4 N[15].

When a number of fish is used in a survival-time experiment, even when a standardization has been adopted for size, acclimatization time, etc., it is found that there is an individual variation in their degree of resistance. Herbert and Merkens[6] have made some important observations on this factor in their study of the toxicity of cyanide solutions to trout. For each of the concentrations tested they used a large number of fish, generally 40 or more, and graphs were drawn showing the percentage of fish overturned plotted against time. *Figure 16* is one of these graphs and it will be seen that the points lie on a sigmoid curve. The median time, the time at which 50 per cent of the fish have overturned, is about 80 min, and it will be noted that the points are not symmetrically disposed relative to this point on the time scale. The first fish overturned in about 24 min

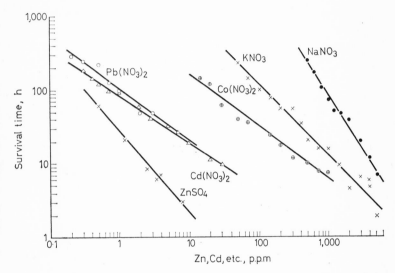

Figure 21. Survival time–concentration data for the rainbow trout in solutions of zinc sulphate at 17·5° C, drawn from the data of Lloyd[13]; and for sticklebacks in solutions of various metallic salts at 15–18° C

but the last did not do so until over 200 min. Accordingly, if a frequency polygon is constructed in which the numbers overturning in successive intervals of time are plotted against time, it is found that this polygon is not symmetrical; the distribution of the times is not 'normal'. This is why it is considered preferable to use geometric means rather than arithmetic means of the survival times in the construction of the survival curve.

Fish removed from cyanide solutions immediately they overturn recover very quickly when placed in fresh water. This enabled Herbert and Merkens to make a series of successive tests upon the same batch of 50 trout, which were marked so that they could be individually identified. Eight tests were made over a three-week period and it was found that though the results were not exactly the same there was an obvious tendency for any one fish to retain its original position in the overturning order. Thus variation in survival time is not a short-lived random effect of the environment; different fish have different degrees of resistance, a resistance which would seem to be an inherent quality.

Fish may be killed, eventually, by a very low concentration of a poison which does not appear to affect them during an experiment lasting a few days[16] and it is probably true to say that for most toxic substances and fish the threshold concentrations are not known. Much study of pollutants has to take the form of a standardized

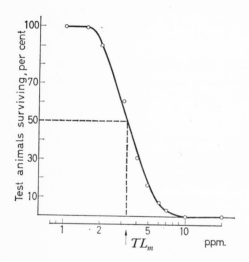

Figure 22. Hypothetical graph to explain the method of determining median tolerance limits. It is assumed that preliminary experiments have shown that the limit lies between 1 and 20 p.p.m.

routine method of toxicity estimation and the generally accepted index of toxicity is the median tolerance limit or TL_m. This is the concentration at which 50 per cent of the test animals survive for a specific period. This may be 24, 48 or 96 h; 24 h would seem a rather inadequate test period and 48 h should be regarded as the minimum time for really useful results. The experimental procedure is simple[2]; on the basis of preliminary experiments a number of solutions is prepared, covering a suitable concentration range and a sufficient number of fish is put into each solution. In 48 or 96 h, as the case may be, the fish are examined and the percentage of survivors for each concentration is noted. The concentration corresponding to 50 per cent survival may be read off the interpolated graph (*Figure 22*).

The main advantage of the procedure is that continuous observation of the fish is not necessary. As discussed earlier in this chapter a standardization should be adopted for the size of the test animals, the temperature, oxygen content and nature of the water used for making up the solutions.

The median tolerance limit, although a valuable measure of toxicity, is not the concentration the fish can be expected to survive for many days or weeks. It has been suggested that permissible concentrations should be one-tenth of the median tolerance limits; Beak[17] considers this to be little more than an intelligent guess. If the toxicity/concentration relationship follows the general equation $C^n T = k$ much depends on the values of the constants n and k. The general level of toxicity of the substance is expressed very largely by the value of the constant k, assuming, of course, that C and T are always expressed in the same units. The other constant n determines the slope of the survival line. Assume as a simple example that $n=1$, then a tenfold reduction in the concentration gives a tenfold increase in the survival time. If $n=3$, reducing the concentration ten times will increase the survival time a thousand times. Thus if the value of n is low the slope of the survival line in the log/log graph is low and the toxicity falls off slowly as the concentration is decreased; if the value of n is high the toxicity declines sharply as the concentration falls. The available evidence shows that different toxic substances vary fairly considerably in this respect; thus in the cyanide toxicity equation of Herbert and Merkens the value of n is over 5, while in the zinc sulphate experiments of Lloyd a tenfold reduction in the concentration prolongs the survival time about ten times so that the value of n is about unity.

REFERENCES

[1] Wuhrmann, K.   Sur quelques principes de la toxicologie des poissons. *Bull. du C.B.E.D.E.* (1952) No. 15

[2] Doudoroff, P., Anderson, B. G., Burdick, G. E., Galtsoff, P. S., Hart, W. B., Patrick, R., Strong, E. R., Surber, E. W. and Van Horn, W. M.   Bioassay methods for the evaluation of acute toxicity of industrial wastes to fish.   *Sewage industr. Wastes*, 23 (1951) 1380–97

[3] Roberts, C. H. and Jee, E. C.   Report No. 39 on the technique of physiological experiments as carried out at the Fisheries Experimental Station of the Ministry of Agriculture and Fisheries at Alresford, Hants. *Salmon and Trout Mag.* 32 (1923) 120–28

[4] Davis, J. T. and Hardcastle, W. S.   Biological assay of herbicides for fish toxicity.   *Weeds*, 7 (1959) 397–404

[5] Wuhrmann, K. and Woker, H.   Statistiche Uberlegungen zu toxicologischen Experimenten und Fischvergiftungen in freien Gewässern. *Schweiz. Z. Hydrol.*, 12 (1950) 271–87

[6] Herbert, D. W. M. and Merkens, J. C. The toxicity of potassium cyanide to trout. *J. exp. Biol.*, 29 (1952) 632–49

[7] Collier, A. and Ray, S. M. An automatic proportioning apparatus for experimental study of the effects of chemical solutions on aquatic animals. *Science*, 107 (1948) 576–7

[8] Warren, E. On the reaction of *Daphnia magna* (Straus) to certain changes in its environment. *Quart. J. micr. Sci.*, 43 n.s. (1900) 199–224

[9] Powers, E. B. The goldfish (*Carassius carassius*) as a test animal in the study of toxicity. *Illinois biol. Monogr.*, 4 (1917) 127–93

[10] Burdick, G. E. A graphical method of deriving threshold values of toxicity and the equation of the toxicity curve. *N.Y. Fish and Game J.*, 4 (1957) 102–8

[11] Hynes, H. B. N. *The Biology of Polluted Waters.* 1960. Liverpool; Liverpool Univ. Press

[12] Herbert, D. W. M. and Downing, K. M. A further study of the toxicity of potassium cyanide to rainbow trout (*Salmo gairdnerii* Richardson). *Ann. appl. Biol.*, 43 (1955) 237–42

[13] Lloyd, R. The toxicity of zinc sulphate to rainbow trout. *Ann. appl. Biol.*, 48 (1960) 84–94

[14] Grindley, J. Toxicity to rainbow trout and minnows of some substances known to be present in waste water discharged to rivers. *Ann. appl. Biol.*, 33 (1946) 103–12

[15] Jones, J. R. E. Antagonism between salts of the heavy and alkaline–earth metals in their toxic action on the tadpole of the toad (*Bufo bufo bufo* L.). *J. exp. Biol.*, 16 (1939) 313–33

[16] Allan, I. R. H., Alabaster, J. S. and Herbert, D. W. M. Recent studies on toxicity and stream pollution. *Water Sanit. Engr.*, 5 (1954) 109–12

[17] Beak, T. W. Toleration of fish to toxic pollution. *J. Fish. Res. Bd. Can.*, 15 (1958) 559–72

5

LEAD, ZINC AND COPPER: THE 'COAGULATION FILM ANOXIA' THEORY

THE pollution of rivers by lead, zinc and other heavy metals has attracted attention for a considerable time. Lead is present in effluents associated with the manufacture of accumulators, in lead paint wastes and wastes from the manufacture of pewter ware. Zinc is present in effluents associated with the manufacture of rubber and the processes of zinc-plating and galvanizing. The main sources of pollution by heavy metals, however, are the mines where their ores are crushed and washed. Many of the lead mines in the British Isles are very old. It is believed that some of those in Cardiganshire date back to Roman and pre-Roman times but it was during the nineteenth century, when the industry became greatly developed and fine-grinding machinery was introduced, that the crushing and washing of lead, zinc and silver ores began to give rise to serious pollution.

A great deal of information about the state of the rivers of the lead-mining districts in these times is to be found in the fifth report of the River Pollution Commission of 1874[1]. The affected streams are described as turbid, whitened by the waste of the lead mines in their courses, bringing down 'slimes' at flood time which were spread over the fields, fouling and destroying the grass. Accounts are given of healthy rivers abounding in salmon, sea-trout and trout being turned into barren watercourses with loose bottoms shifting at every flood, of cattle being killed by eating the fouled grass and horses being made paralysed and broken winded. Fowls were killed by pecking in the lead-polluted grit; ducks and geese, probably due to their natural habits, were particularly liable to poisoning and became paralysed after going to the river. The basic method of extracting the ores was to crush and grind the mined material to a fine state of division and then subject it to washing and flotation so that the lighter, earthy matter was washed away from the heavier ores. The washing water contained great quantities of very finely divided, suspended matter. Efforts were made to prevent this from reaching the rivers by leading the water through settling pits, where the 'slimes' settled. The material cleaned out from the settling pits and great quantities of gravel, mined material too poor in ore to be worth washing, and other mineral waste in all stages of division were piled up to form the great, grey 'dumps' which are such a conspicuous feature of the valleys of lead-mining districts. For the provision of washing water many small dams were built across the stream valleys above the mines, sometimes with long aqueducts. The reasons for the introduction of the settling pits are not very clear. It seems that in the early days of the industry the washing water ran straight into the rivers into which was cast, also, all the unwanted mined material. Perhaps the settling pits were introduced with the idea of preventing pollution. It is also possible that hopes were entertained of extracting more metal ore from the dump material; many such attempts were made after the mines were worked out.

The industry declined towards the end of the nineteenth century and in Cardiganshire all the mines had ceased working when the European war of 1914–18 broke out. The war led to a reopening of some of the mines but they closed again when peace came. All the affected rivers in Cardiganshire were then quite devoid of fish and very lacking in flora and invertebrate fauna. Larger rivers in neighbouring districts of Wales, such as the Dovey, had been damaged to some extent. While it was generally accepted that the mining operations were responsible for the absence of fish there was a complete lack of understanding of the nature of the toxic processes involved. Carpenter[2-4], who began her studies of the polluted Cardiganshire rivers in 1919, noted that in 1922, following the cessation of mining operations, a considerable improvement in the flora and invertebrate fauna had taken place. Despite this increase in the available food supply no fish had become established, and Carpenter decided to carry out some experiments to find out whether the river water was toxic to fish. In August 1923 minnows were placed in a fish cage in the river Rheidol, about 7 m. above the sea. At this time the river, when at normal level, contained no lead in solution, but 0·2–0·5 p.p.m. might be present when it was in flood.

For some weeks the minnows lived, but in the autumn, when the river was in flood, they died. The experiment was repeated with minnows and with yearling trout with the same result. The fish died at time of flood when the river contained lead in solution. Its presence in the flood water is easily explained. In the mine dumps, during dry weather, finely divided residues of lead sulphide became oxidized to lead sulphate, which is sufficiently soluble to be leached out by heavy rain and carried down to the river. Carpenter's experiments with the fish cage thus showed that the absence of fish from the Cardiganshire rivers was associated with the presence of dissolved lead, and was not the result of purely physical injury to the gills by gritty particles, as had been suggested. A few years earlier Powers[5] had published his classic study on the effects of toxic substances on the goldfish and this prompted Carpenter to carry out some laboratory experiments on the effects of heavy metal salts on fish, using minnows as test animals[6]. Survival and fatality curves were worked out for sodium chloride and proved to be similar in general character to those obtained by Powers for the goldfish, but lead nitrate gave a fatality curve of a completely different type. The reciprocals of the survival times plotted against the concentration (*Figure 23*) follow a

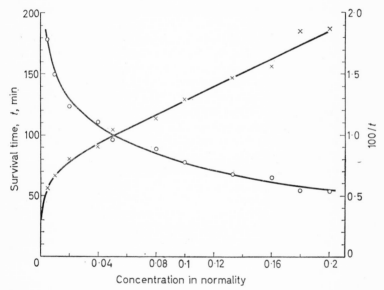

Figure 23. Survival and fatality curves for minnows in solutions of lead nitrate at 16·5–17·5° C

(Drawn from the data of Carpenter[6].)

straight line over the greater part of the concentration range, but this straight line cuts the time axis and not the concentration axis as in Powers' curves. Thus there was no 'theoretical threshold of toxicity'. The new form of the fatality curve 'suggested that the entire quality of the lead-reaction might be of a type not hitherto described'.

Carpenter noticed that in the lead solutions the fish died with symptoms of acute respiratory distress. The body became covered with a veil-like film, which looked like coagulated mucus; within the operculum the gills were seen to be covered by a thicker film of apparently similar nature, and when, after death, the fish, after washing in distilled water, was treated with a dilute solution of ammonium sulphide, this film turned black, indicating the presence of lead. Similar symptoms were seen in the fish that died in the fish cages. Death, therefore, seemed to be the result of asphyxiation, brought on by the heavy metal ions reacting with some constituent of the mucus secreted by the gills. Further work[6,7] with salts of other heavy metals—zinc, copper, cadmium and mercury—suggested a similar form of toxic reaction. The relation between survival time and concentration could be expressed by the equation $K = 1/t \log 1/\text{conc.}$, the value of K ranging from 0·013 in the case of lead and zinc to 0·10 for mercury. with the survival times in minutes and the concentration in normality.

Ellis[8] agreed with Carpenter's conclusions and considered that acids and other chemicals such as trinitrophenol killed fish in the same way. The chief heavy metal salt studied by Ellis was copper sulphate. He pointed out that the toxic process is threefold in its attack on the respiratory apparatus. First, the spaces between the gill filaments become filled with precipitate, so that the water flowing through the branchial chambers cannot reach the gill filament cells; secondly, the spaces between the gill lamellae become filled so that movement of the gill filaments becomes impossible, and this condition affects the circulation of the blood in the gill capillaries; thirdly, this stasis affecting the blood circulation in the gills leads to heart block, the heart action dropping to about half the normal rate. Ellis also concluded that certain polluting substances which do not precipitate the gill secretions can cause death by direct damage to the gill filament cells, and that this might be a rapid or a slow process. The 'coagulation film anoxia' theory was also supported by Dilling, Healey and Smith[9], Westfall[10] and Schweiger[11].

When Carpenter took up the study of the toxic action of lead salts on fish the presence of zinc salts in the affected rivers was suspected, but methods for the detection and estimation of small quantities of this metal were not available at the time. It is quite possible that at the time of Carpenter's investigations the polluted rivers were affected by zinc even more than by lead. At the present time the Rheidol, the largest river in north Cardiganshire, is virtually free from metallic pollution, but the neighbouring river Ystwyth was polluted with lead and zinc in 1940[12], and in 1956 still carried up to 0·6 p.p.m. of zinc[13]. This extraordinary persistence of the pollution 35 years after the cessation of mining activities, for the last mines in the Ystwyth valley were abandoned in 1921, and some 80 years after the peak period of the industry, requires some explanation. Of the ores mined the silver ore was the most prized but the silver was rapidly exhausted;

the lead was also valued highly, and probably every effort was made in the crushing and washing to extract as much galena as possible before the discarded material was dumped. It is quite possible that great quantities of mined material containing zinc ore but too poor in lead to be worth washing, were never processed but thrown on the dumps or into old shafts. Blende is a much lighter mineral than galena and so the simple water flotation process used in the early days of the industry, while effecting a reasonably good separation of lead ore from earthy matter, was far less satisfactory in the case of the zinc ore. Lastly, blende is a much more stable compound than galena; undergoing oxidation and leaching out much more slowly; thus it is not surprising that a great reserve of zinc remains at the derelict mines.

Carpenter carried out no experiments with zinc solutions at concentrations below 0·005 N (about 160 p.p.m. Zn). The writer[14] has shown that zinc sulphate solutions are toxic to sticklebacks down to a concentration of about 0·3 p.p.m. Zn when a very soft water is used for making up the solutions. The limit for lead is about 0·1 p.p.m. In the presence of calcium salts the toxicity of lead and zinc is much reduced. A 1·0 p.p.m. lead solution (lead nitrate) is fatal to sticklebacks in 18–28 h. The addition of 50 p.p.m. of calcium, as calcium chloride or calcium nitrate, will prolong the survival time to over 10 days (*Figure 24*). The same amount of calcium will bring about a similar reduction in the toxicity of zinc sulphate solutions of concentration 2·0 p.p.m. Zn. The action is not one dependent on precipitation, for calcium nitrate could not precipitate either metal and the nature of the protective effect has not been explained. It is known, however, that the calcium ion is of great importance in preserving the stability of epithelial tissue[15].

Ellis[8] also noted the effect of calcium in reducing the toxicity of a heavy metal, in this case copper. His experiments were made with goldfish and 10 p.p.m. copper solutions ($CuSO_4$). Different amounts of sodium nitrate were added and this brought about a reduction of the toxicity, which was further reduced by the addition of calcium chloride. Ellis does not appear to have tested the effect of adding calcium chloride alone. There is evidence that this property of calcium is shared by related metals. The writer[16] has shown that the toxicity of copper solutions to tadpoles is reduced by the addition of salts of magnesium, calcium, strontium or barium.

Work in Australia by Affleck[17] has shown that zinc is highly toxic to the ova and young stages of rainbow trout and brown trout. Affleck's investigation was prompted by the heavy mortality observed in trout hatcheries where galvanized pipes were used for the water supply. The water used at the hatchery was very soft, containing

57

only 1·7 p.p.m. of calcium, so that it tended to pick up zinc from the supply pipes, from galvanized iron containers and from the galvanized iron gauze used to support the ova in the hatching troughs. In glass hatching troughs in which the eggs rested on galvanized iron gauze none survived to the eyed stage and painting the gauze with aluminium paint effected little improvement; 95 per cent of the eggs hatched when they rested on muslin. In an experiment with newly

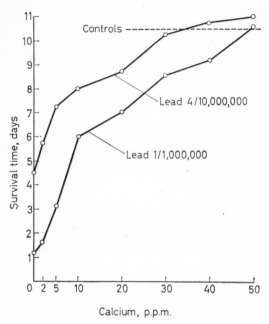

Figure 24. Prolongation of the survival time of sticklebacks in lead nitrate solutions on the addition of calcium chloride

(By courtesy of the *Journal of Experimental Biology*.)

hatched alevins of rainbow trout only 286 out of 626 survived more than 28 days in a concrete pond supplied with water running through a galvanized iron pipe. A control experiment in which the water ran through a rubber hose gave a 98 per cent survival. The zinc present in the first case is given as 0·01 p.p.m.; in the second, 0·003 p.p.m. Where the zinc came from in the second experiment is not explained; the two tests were not carried out with the same pond. Further experiments with fingerling rainbow trout showed that some mortality occurred after the fish were kept for a short period in galvanized iron pails used for transport. Symptoms of poisoning developed some hours after the fish were removed from the cans and placed in water not contaminated by zinc.

Affected alevins, fry and fingerlings tended to be darker in colour than normal specimens; often they appeared to be partially paralysed on one side so that their equilibrium was affected and they tended to swim in fits and starts and in spirals. Respiratory distress was evident and a coating of mucus was formed over the gills. In the affected eggs a whitish, cloudy opacity was visible through the chorion in the perivitelline space during the late eyed stage. Dead embryos sometimes burst out, usually yolk-sac, or head, first. Affleck carried out no experiments with prepared solutions of zinc salts.

The toxicity of copper salts to fish is interesting not only because of the occurrence of copper in mine effluents and trade wastes, but because copper sulphate is used on a large scale as an algicide in lakes and reservoirs. It is considered to be very suitable for the control of algae because it forms heavy, insoluble compounds with the proteins and other constituents of algal cells, compounds which sink to the bottom and are removed from the main mass of water[18]. Its use is a hazard to fish and there have been many studies of its toxicity, with rather varied results, which have been reviewed by Doudoroff and Katz[19]. The limiting concentrations for various fish given by various authors cover the surprising range of 0·02 to 200 p.p.m. It is not certain, in some cases, whether the concentrations given are p.p.m. copper or p.p.m. $CuSO_45H_2O$ and in some experiments, at least, hard waters were used for making up the solutions, with the result that most of the copper was precipitated. Again some of the results discussed involved test periods of only 24 h, and in some instances the investigators gave no information at all about the duration of their experiments. After their examination of all the data Doudoroff and Katz conclude that in most of the natural fresh waters of the U.S.A. copper sulphate concentrations below 0·025 p.p.m. as Cu are not rapidly fatal for most of the common fish species.

Recent research on the toxicity of lead, zinc and copper to fish has gone along three main lines. Further study has been made of the way the toxicity of the solution is influenced by the degree of hardness of the water; the coagulation film anoxia theory has been subjected to a re-examination, and thirdly the toxicity of solutions containing both copper and zinc has been tested. In experiments on rainbow trout with lead nitrate[20] it was found that with water of hardness 14 p.p.m. as $CaCO_3$ all the lead added remained in solution; some precipitation of the lead occurred with water of hardness 27 p.p.m., when the lead concentration exceeded 8 p.p.m. In still harder water containing

53 p.p.m. Ca as $CaCO_3$ most of the lead was precipitated and not more than 1·6 p.p.m. remained in solution. The precipitated lead appeared to be non-toxic. The solutions made up with the soft water were toxic to the rainbow trout down to a concentration of rather less than 1 p.p.m. (*Figure 25*).

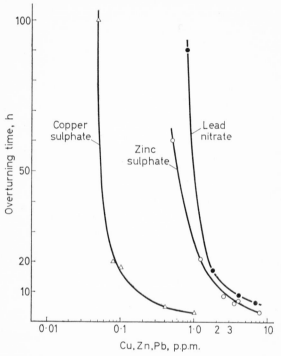

Figure 25. Survival curves for rainbow trout in solutions of zinc sulphate at 17·5° C, drawn from the data of Lloyd[21]; and for rainbow trout in copper sulphate (17·5° C) and lead nitrate (18·5° C), drawn from the data in Water Pollution Research, 1959[20]

Experiments on the same lines with copper sulphate gave rather similar results. Solutions made up with soft water (12 p.p.m. as $CaCO_3$) were toxic to rainbow trout down to about 0·06 p.p.m. Cu. The use of a very hard water (320 p.p.m. as $CaCO_3$) resulted in a very great reduction of the toxicity, the limiting concentration going up to about 0·6 p.p.m. Above 2·5 p.p.m. the copper tended to precipitate from solution. Whether the precipitate is toxic is not known.

A recent study of the toxicity of zinc sulphate to the rainbow trout is that by Lloyd[21]. The nature of the water used for making up the solutions was again found to influence the results very considerably. With a soft water, hardness 12 p.p.m. as $CaCO_3$, the log/log graph of the concentrations and survival times is linear (*Figure 21*) so that the relation corresponds to the equation $C^n T = k$. The log/log graphs for solutions with hard waters, 50 and 320 p.p.m. as $CaCO_3$, are curved; they conform well to the equation $(C-a)^n(T-b) = K$ if the threshold concentrations are taken to be 1·5 and 3·5 p.p.m. Zn and the threshold reaction times are taken as 140 and 160 min.

The threshold concentrations remain much the same at higher temperatures but the survival times are shorter, and a reduction of the oxygen available also shortens the survival time. In the hard water the zinc tends to be precipitated and the precipitated zinc appears to be toxic, for if it is increased in amount the survival time shortens though the concentration of zinc in solution remains much the same. Lloyd observed no precipitation of mucus on the gills of the trout treated with zinc sulphate and considers that the death of the fish should be attributed to damage to the gill tissues, as suggested by Ellis[8]. Histological examination of the gills of rainbow trout treated with solutions of lead, zinc and copper salts tends to confirm this[22]. The epithelium separates from the gill filaments and from the lamellae; the cells are sloughed off into the spaces between the filaments, where they break down. Serious damage becomes evident when about half the expected survival time has expired, and when the fish overturn about half the respiratory epithelium has been destroyed.

It is possible that the exact nature of the toxic action of heavy metal ions on fish depends on the nature and quantity of their gill secretions. It may be that some species produce relatively little secretion, and that a rapid disintegration of the gill tissues results from exposure to heavy metal salts. Others may produce a copious secretion which may protect the epithelium from damage but which, when precipitated, leads to asphyxiation. The goldfish appears to be a type in which the gill secretions are abundant; in a dilute lead nitrate solution, 10 p.p.m. Pb in soft water, so much precipitated mucus is formed that the solution becomes milky and a white sediment collects on the bottom of the vessel[14]. Some interesting experiments have recently been carried out with lampreys by Sawyer[23]. Calcium hydroxide, described as a slime-stimulating compound, brought about death in *Petromyzon marinus*, the sea-lamprey, in 11 h at 50 p.p.m. The whole animal was covered with a thin film of coagulated slime, but the gills were undamaged and the epidermis was intact. On the other hand the fungicide zinc dimethyldithiocarbamate, which was fatal in 6 h at 0.5 p.p.m., appeared to be very destructive to the gill tissues. Sections showed that the gills were completely destroyed as functional units.

The information in the literature about the nature and functions of the mucus secreted by fish has been reviewed by Van Oosten[24]. It is known to be produced by the secretion of mucin by epidermal cells. The mucin, produced as globules or long threads, forms a clear, lubricating slime on mixing with the water. In general, the amount of mucus produced by fish bears an inverse relationship to the extent to which the body is protected by scales; the fish with a naked skin producing much slime, the heavily scaled types comparatively little. Chemical analysis shows that the slime is largely albuminous in nature, and like egg albumen it is precipitated as a dense, whitish cloud on the addition of a solution of a heavy metal salt. The functions it performs in fish appear to be many. It is believed to reduce body friction in swimming and to protect the animal from the attacks of parasites and micro-organisms. It also seems to have the power of precipitating fine suspended matter, and fish that produce much slime are said to survive in muddy water better than those producing little. The secretion of mucus by the gills prevents fine particles of matter from sticking to them. Finally, the mucus may play some part in controlling the permeability of the integument to salts and other substances. The available evidence, here, is not all in agreement, but it seems that elvers can only adapt themselves to changes in salinity while their coat of slime remains intact; the mucus secretions of the stickleback are known to impede the passage of chloride ions, and the Pacific salmon immediately increases its own production of slime when it returns to fresh water to spawn.

While the precise nature of the toxic effect of heavy metal salts on fish may need further investigation their general effect on the animal's respiration is very clear. It is a fairly simple matter to set up apparatus with which periodic measurements can be made of the oxygen consumption of a fish immersed in a solution of a heavy metal salt[25]. In addition, the accompanying changes in the rate of the breathing movements can be observed. Two typical results of experiments with sticklebacks are given in *Figure 26*. The solutions are 0·002 N $CuSO_4$ and 0·005 N $Pb(NO_3)_2$. These concentrations are much higher than what would be encountered in natural waters; they are equivalent to about 64 p.p.m. Cu and 500 p.p.m. Pb, but experiments at lower concentrations have a similar result, with the time scale extended.

Normally the stickleback 'breathes' about 120 times per min at 17° C. When the heavy metal salt is run into the apparatus the rate of opercular movement and the rate of oxygen consumption rise; this is the result of increased activity, for the fish seems to sense the unfavourable change in its environment and will struggle. As the toxic process advances the respiratory movements become more and more rapid, more regular and of increased amplitude. Despite the animal's efforts to maintain its oxygen supply the oxygen consumption falls, returns to normal, and becomes sub-normal. After periods of struggling and rest, and minor ups and downs in the opercular

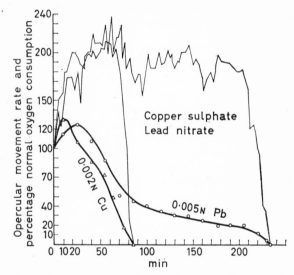

Figure 26. Oxygen consumption (heavy) and opercular movement rate (light) curves for sticklebacks in 0·002 N copper sulphate and 0·005 N lead nitrate. Temperature 17° C

(By courtesy of the *Journal of Experimental Biology.*)

movement rate, the fish sooner or later becomes exhausted; when the oxygen consumption rate sinks to about 20 per cent of normal the opercular movement rate begins a precipitous descent and the fish dies.

A new paper by Crandall and Goodnight[26] describes an investigation of the long-term effects of 'sub-lethal' concentrations of lead nitrate and zinc sulphate on the guppy. The selected concentrations are stated to be 2 and 5 p.p.m. of lead nitrate, and 5 and 10 p.p.m. of zinc sulphate, but the values quoted seem somewhat uncertain; the 5 p.p.m. lead nitrate solution is said to be equivalent to 2·48 p.p.m. as lead—this should be 3·12 p.p.m. The water used for making up the solutions had a total hardness of 80 p.p.m. and observations were made over periods ranging up to 129 days. Fish were removed periodically and sectioned for histological examination. Several histological changes were observed, including lack of mesenteric fat, reduction of renal peritubular lymphoid tissue, an apparent dilatation of renal tubules and retarded gonadal development. In addition there were indications of cardiac damage and blood cell destruction. The authors conclude that the histopathology and retardation of sexual maturity suggest that the secondary effects of inanition and/or stress were the most important features of the chronic intoxication. There was no demonstrable, consistent alteration of the respiratory epithelium, or mucous accumulations indicating damage to the respiratory surfaces, but some of the sections showed granular debris in the branchial blood vessels.

Copper sulphate and zinc sulphate dissolved in soft water have been shown to have a synergistic action, i.e. their combined action is more than additive. Thus Doudoroff[27] found that while minnows (*Pimephales*) survived for about 8 h in an 8 p.p.m. zinc solution or a 0·2 p.p.m. copper solution a mixed solution containing only 1 p.p.m. zinc and 0·025 p.p.m. copper was rather more toxic. Lead, on the other hand, reduces the toxicity of copper to freshwater invertebrates[28]; this is an example of antagonism. Synergism and antagonism are discussed in Chapter 15.

Of the three heavy metals discussed in this chapter, copper is the most toxic to trout, the lethal limits for lead and zinc being very similar for water of the same degree of hardness[29]. The relative toxicity of the metals is more fully discussed in the next chapter, which also deals with the reactions of fish to lead, zinc and copper.

REFERENCES

[1] Rivers Pollution Commission appointed in 1868. Fifth report (1874). Vol. 1, Report and maps; Vol. 2, Evidence

[2] Carpenter, K. E. A study of the fauna of rivers polluted by lead mining in the Aberystwyth district of Cardiganshire. *Ann. appl. Biol.*, 11 (1924) 1–23

[3] Carpenter, K. E. On the biological factors involved in the destruction of river-fisheries by pollution due to lead-mining. *Ann. appl. Biol.*, 12 (1925) 1–13

[4] Carpenter, K. E. The lead mine as an active agent in river pollution. *Ann. appl. Biol.*, 13 (1926) 395–401

[5] Powers, E. B. The goldfish (*Carassius carassius*) as a test animal in the study of toxicity. *Illinois biol. Monogr.*, 4 (1917) 127–93

[6] Carpenter, K. E. The lethal action of soluble metallic salts on fishes. *Brit. J. exp. Biol.*, 4 (1927) 378–90

[7] Carpenter, K. E. Further researches on the action of metallic salts on fishes. *J. exp. Zool.*, 56 (1930) 407–22

LEAD, ZINC AND COPPER

8 Ellis, M. M. Detection and measurement of stream pollution. *Bull. U.S. Bur. Fish.*, 48 (1937) 365–437

9 Dilling, W. J., Healey, C. W. and Smith, W. C. Experiments on the effect of lead on the growth of plaice (*Pleuronectes platessa*). *Ann. appl. Biol.*, 13 (1926) 168–76

10 Westfall, B. A. Coagulation film anoxia in fishes. *Ecology*, 26 (1945) 283–7

11 Schweiger, G. Die toxicologische Einwirkung von Schwermetallsalzen auf Fische und Fischnährtiere. *Arch. Fischereiwissenschaft*, 8 (1957) 54–78

12 Jones, J. R. E. A study of the zinc-polluted river Ystwyth in north Cardiganshire, Wales. *Ann. appl. Biol.*, 27 (1940) 367–78

13 Jones, J. R. E. A further study of the zinc-polluted river Ystwyth. *J. anim. Ecol.*, 27 (1958) 1–14

14 Jones, J. R. E. The relative toxicity of salts of lead, zinc and copper to the stickleback (*Gasterosteus aculeatus* L.) and the effect of calcium on the toxicity of lead and zinc salts. *J. exp. Biol.*, 15 (1938) 394–407

15 Hober, R. *Physical Chemistry of Cells and Tissues.* 1945. London; Churchill

16 Jones, J. R. E. Antagonism between salts of the heavy and alkaline-earth metals in their toxic action on the tadpole of the toad (*Bufo bufo bufo* L.). *J. exp. Biol.*, 16 (1939) 313–33

17 Affleck, R. J. Zinc poisoning in a trout hatchery. *Aust. J. Mar. Freshw. Res.*, 3 (1952) 142–69

18 Pearsall, W. H., Gardiner, A. C. and Greenshields, F. Freshwater biology and water supply in Britain. *Sci. Publ. Freshw. Biol. Ass. Brit. Empire*, No. 11 (1946) 90 pp.

19 Doudoroff, P. and Katz, M. Critical review of literature on the toxicity of industrial wastes and their components to fish, II. Metals as salts. *Sewage industr. Wastes*, 25 (1953) 802–39

20 *Water Pollution Research, 1959.* 1960. London; H.M.S.O.

21 Lloyd, R. The toxicity of zinc sulphate to rainbow trout. *Ann. appl. Biol.*, 48 (1960) 84–94

22 *Water Pollution Research, 1960.* 1961. London; H.M.S.O.

23 Sawyer, P. J. Effect of certain chemicals on mucus-producing cells of *Petromyzon marinus*. *Trans. Amer. Fish. Soc.*, 88 (1959) 305–9

24 Van Oosten, J. The skin and scales. In *The Physiology of Fishes, Volume 1—Metabolism*, ed. by Margaret E. Brown, 1957. New York; Academic Press

25 Jones, J. R. E. The oxygen consumption of *Gasterosteus aculeatus* L. in toxic solutions. *J. exp. Biol.*, 23 (1947) 298–311

26 Crandall, C. A. and Goodnight, C. J. The effects of sub-lethal concentrations of several toxicants to the common guppy, *Lebistes reticulatus*. *Trans. Amer. Microsc. Soc.*, 82 (1963) 59–73

27 Doudoroff, P. Some recent developments in the study of toxic industrial wastes. *Proc. 4th Pacific North West Industr. Waste Conf., State Coll. of Washington, Pullman, Wash.*, (1952) 21–5

28 Jones, J. R. E. Antagonism between two heavy metals in their toxic action on fresh-water animals. *Proc. Zool. Soc. Lond., Ser A,* 108 (1938) 481–99

29 *Water Pollution Research, 1961.* 1962. London; H.M.S.O.

6

THE METALS AS SALTS

Comparative and general studies

SALTS of the metals may be toxic to fish in three ways: (1) The essential factor may be the cation, the anion being relatively unimportant; lead nitrate, zinc sulphate and copper sulphate, considered in the last chapter, belong in this category. (2) The essential factor may be the anion, or the acid formed from the anion by hydrolysis; to this class belong salts like sodium chromate and the respiratory depressants, potassium cyanide and sodium sulphide, discussed in Chapter 7. (3) The toxic action may be physical, rather than chemical. Bert[1] concluded that when freshwater fish are placed in sea-water the high osmotic pressure of the medium results in an extensive withdrawal of water from the gill tissues, with the result that the afferent and efferent arteries are obliterated by the pressure of the shrinking surrounding tissues, and death results from the arrest of the branchial circulation. This conclusion has been endorsed by Garrey[2] who found that fresh-water fish will readily tolerate diluted sea-water, or similar 'balanced' solutions, of an osmotic pressure equal to that of their blood, but that higher concentrations are rapidly fatal.

The heavy metals, mercury, cadmium, nickel, cobalt, gold, silver and manganese have not been studied to the same extent as lead, zinc and copper, but the available evidence suggests that the toxic action of their salts is of the same general nature: damage to the gill tissues, the formation of a film of coagulated mucus, or both, bringing about death by asphyxiation. *Figure 27* shows the effect of a solution of mercuric chloride on *Gasterosteus*; the general result up to 50 min resembles that shown in *Figure 26*, for lead and copper, but at this point the mercury solution is replaced by water and the fish begins to recover.

In *Figure 28* a series of survival curves is drawn for salts of silver, mercury, cadmium, nickel, cobalt and manganese, and for chlorauric acid[3]. The time scale is linear but a logarithmic scale is used for the concentrations in order to cover the necessary range. Each point represents the mean survival time, not overturning time, of five sticklebacks. The solutions were made up with a very soft tap-water except for the most concentrated of the silver nitrate solutions. The solubility of silver chloride is about 1·5 mg AgCl/l. and so the

66

chlorides in tap-water do not precipitate the silver when the concentration of this ion is well below 1 p.p.m. The series of gold and silver solutions was kept in the dark; chlorauric acid $HAuCl_4$ was used instead of gold chloride $AuCl_3$ as it is a more stable compound. The fish, all 30–50 mm in length, were taken from the same ditch and not kept in the laboratory for more than three or four days before use. The whole series of experiments covered by *Figure 28* was run within a period of 4–5 weeks in order for the results to be comparative.

As these metals are believed to have the same kind of toxic action on fish it might be expected that they should exhibit a similarity in degree of toxicity. This is not so; the different curves are well

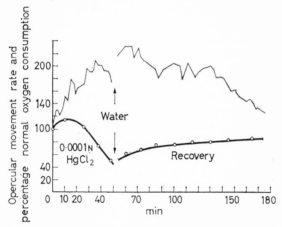

Figure 27. Oxygen consumption and opercular movement rate curves for a stickleback immersed in 0·0001 N mercuric chloride for 50 min, after which the solution is replaced by water and the fish recovers

(By courtesy of the *Journal of Experimental Biology.*)

separated, for the most part, on the concentration scale. The dotted perpendiculars indicate the concentrations at which the survival times are about 10 days, and if these values are taken to be the approximate thresholds the limits cover a very wide range: from 40 p.p.m. in the case of manganese down to 0·003 p.p.m. for silver. The toxicity of silver solutions is extremely high; at 10 p.p.m. the survival time is only 25 min and at 1 p.p.m. about an hour. Mercury comes next to silver; then copper, aluminium and lead, curves for which are not included in *Figure 28*. It will be noticed that nickel is very much more toxic than cobalt and it is a little surprising that this should be so as the two metals are so closely related.

A number of the metals included in this study occur in trade wastes.

Mercury occurs in wastes from paper mills and the manufacture of insecticides and fungicides; nickel and cadmium are used for plating; cobalt in the manufacture of pigments. The high toxicity of these and other metals, to fish and other forms of life, has led to much research on the development of methods for detecting and estimating

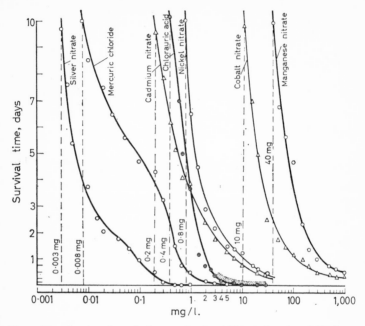

Figure 28. A series of survival curves for the stickleback in salts of the heavy metals. The curves are plotted to dilutions at which the survival times of the fish are approximately equal to that of controls in tap-water—about 10 days. The thresholds indicated by the dotted vertical lines are mg/l., or p.p.m. of silver, mercury, cadmium, etc., not mg/l. of salt. The solutions of chlorauric acid (gold chloride) were sufficiently acid to be fatal at high concentrations; the relevant portion of this survival curve is indicated by shading. pH of all other solutions, within the range 6·0–6·8. Temperature 15–18° C

(By courtesy of the *Journal of Experimental Biology*).

them at great dilution, and many organic reagents have been produced for the purpose[4].

Salts of lead, zinc, copper and the series of metals covered by *Figure 28* hydrolyse to some extent, but there is little or no evidence to suggest that the acidity of the solutions, resulting from this hydrolysis, is sufficiently high to be a lethal factor, except, perhaps, at very high concentrations. The soluble salts of iron, chromium and aluminium hydrolyse to a much greater extent. Ferric chloride solutions have a toxicity to *Gasterosteus* which is similar to that of hydrochloric acid solutions of the same pH, which suggests that trivalent iron has a very low toxicity.　Divalent (ferrous) iron can cause trouble as it acts as a reducing agent; when oxidized it forms ferric hydroxide, which is precipitated as a red-brown slime.　This type of pollution is mainly

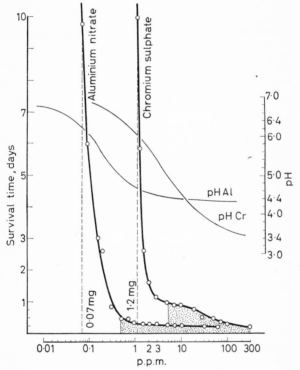

Figure 29. Survival curves for sticklebacks in aluminium nitrate and chromium sulphate and the pH variation of the solutions.　The portions of the survival curves bounded by shading cover the concentration ranges over which the solutions are sufficiently acid to be fatal.　Concentrations are p.p.m. Al, Cr.　Temperature 15–18° C

(By courtesy of the *Journal of Experimental Biology*.)

associated with mine-water, which may contain over 2,000 p.p.m. of ferrous iron[4].　Chromium sulphate and aluminium nitrate are markedly toxic at dilutions where the hydrogen ion concentration is within the tolerated range; for the stickleback this is about pH 5·0–11·4.　The toxicity of aluminium to the stickleback appears to be very high; the limiting concentration, at 0·07 p.p.m. Al, is below that for lead (*Figure 29*).

A further series of survival curves for *Gasterosteus* is given in *Figure 30*, in this case for the metals of the alkalis and alkaline earths[3]. It should be noted that the concentration scale is in grammes per litre or parts per thousand; these metals are very much less toxic than the

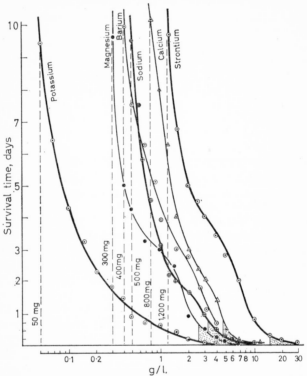

Figure 30.   Survival curves for sticklebacks in solutions of potassium nitrate, sodium nitrate, magnesium nitrate, calcium nitrate, strontium nitrate and barium nitrate.   The shaded portions of the survival curves indicate the concentration ranges over which the solutions are hypertonic.   pH of calcium solutions 6·8–8·6.   Extreme pH range of all other solutions 6·0–6·8.   Temperature 15–18° C

(By courtesy of the *Journal of Experimental Biology*.)

heavy metals, with the exception of potassium, whose toxicity approaches that of manganese.   The lethal action of these salts appears to be different in nature from that of salts of the heavy metals; the gills of fish killed by toxic concentrations are clean and red, and the gill filaments are free.   The question arises as to how far the toxicity of salts of this group can be attributed to osmotic pressure, to the physical rather than chemical action described at the beginning of this chapter. The osmotic pressure of the blood of freshwater teleost fish is about 6 atm. The osmotic pressures of the sodium, calcium, magnesium and strontium solutions have been calculated in the usual way from the G factors and the molar concentrations, and the concentration ranges over which the solutions were hypertonic (i.e. had an osmotic pressure higher than 6 atm.) are indicated in *Figure 30*. It will be seen that all four salts are distinctly toxic at concentrations well below isotonicity. The potassium and barium solutions were all hypotonic. Osmotic pressure therefore cannot account for the death of the fish, except at the highest concentrations where it may play some part in the toxic process. At very high concentrations of these salts the survival time may be very short; thus a 20,000 p.p.m. sodium solution ($NaNO_3$) is fatal in about 26 min.

According to Goodman and Gilman[5] the potassium ion, although necessary for cell function, is highly toxic in excess of the normal requirements, with marked effects on muscular and nervous activity; death may result from cardiac depression. Soluble barium salts are generally regarded as highly poisonous to the higher animals, their toxic property being attributed to the violent and indiscriminate stimulation they impart to all kinds of involuntary muscle. It is generally believed that the integument of teleost fish is completely impermeable to salts. The urine of freshwater fish is dilute and copious though they swallow very little water; this seems to indicate that they absorb a considerable amount of water through the gills as suggested by Smith[6], but whether salts enter the body in this way is not known. Ellis[7] believed that the external structures (the gills) of fish would admit 'volatile' compounds such as chlorine, ether, methyl mercaptan, formaldehyde and chloroform, but that other toxic chemicals, which did not bring about death by injury to the gills, entered the body by way of the gastrointestinal tract. Ellis states that many cumulative poisons enter the body of a fish in this way, but arsenic is the only substance he mentions specifically. Using 'colloidal dye methods' he found that many fish refuse to swallow water containing various types of effluents, for some time, but eventually do swallow a little, even if not fed.

Physiologists have made many attempts to establish a relationship between the physical and chemical properties of the metals and the degree of toxicity of their salts, and their views have varied from time to time to fit new physical conceptions of the elements. Richet[8] studied the relative toxicity of the metals to the heart of the frog, to see whether there was a relation between toxicity and atomic weight, and decided there was no agreement. Other hypotheses have been based on solubility, valency and the periodic table of Mendelejeff. One of the most interesting of these theories is that of Mathews[9] who considered that the physiological effects of ions are governed by their affinity for their electrical charges, and that a relationship therefore exists between the solution pressures of metals and the degree of toxicity of their salts. The solution pressure theory of Nernst attributes to metals a property called solution pressure or solution tension, by virtue of which they tend to pass into solution as positively charged ions. Metals in which this tendency is great (Na, K, Ca, Sr, Ba) have a high solution pressure and so react readily with water to form hydroxides; metals with somewhat lower solution pressures, such as magnesium and zinc, will decompose steam when heated, and react readily with dilute acids; at the other end of the scale are metals like copper and silver which only react with difficulty with strong acids.

Mathews considered that the solution pressure of a metal can be regarded as a measure of its tendency, when in the ionic state as a dissolved salt, to give up its positive charge and enter into combination with other ions or compounds. Sodium ions, very reluctant to give up their electrical charges, have a very low toxicity; copper and silver, very ready to abandon them, have a high tendency to form compounds with the proteins of protoplasm. Mathews experimented only with the eggs of the mud-minnow, *Fundulus*; the writer's study with *Gasterosteus*[3] has shown a measure of agreement between toxicity and solution pressure, but the solution pressure theory of Nernst is now considered obsolete[10].

There have been few other comparative studies of the toxicity of the metals to fish. Doudoroff and Katz[11] discuss the work of Oshima, who tested the toxicity of the chlorides of a number of metals to eels and the cyprinodont fish *Orizias latipes*. In order of decreasing toxicity they formed the series:

$$\text{Hg} > \begin{matrix} \text{Cu} \\ \text{Zn} \\ \text{Cd} \end{matrix} > \begin{matrix} \text{Sn} \\ \text{Al} \\ \text{Ni} \\ \text{Fe}^{+++} \end{matrix} > \text{Fe}^{++} > \text{Ba} > \text{Mn} > \begin{matrix} \text{K} \\ \text{Ca} \\ \text{Mg} \end{matrix} > \text{Na}$$

Symbols grouped vertically indicate metals of similar toxicity. The series bears a close resemblance to the writer's series for *Gasterosteus*. Doudoroff and Katz also discuss the work of Iwao who determined lethal concentrations for *Orizias* based on 24 h tests. In order of decreasing toxicity the metals tested in this case formed the series:

$$\begin{matrix} \text{Hg} \\ \text{Cu} \end{matrix} > \begin{matrix} \text{Au} \\ \text{Pd} \end{matrix} > \text{Th} > \text{Pt} > \text{Cd} > \text{Ce} > \text{Ba} > \begin{matrix} \text{K} \\ \text{Co} \end{matrix} > \begin{matrix} \text{Li} \\ \text{Mn} \end{matrix} > \begin{matrix} \text{Ca} \\ \text{Sr} \end{matrix} > \begin{matrix} \text{Mg} \\ \text{Na} \end{matrix}$$

It is a little difficult to compare this series with that of Oshima as the set of metals selected is not the same. Iwao has omitted zinc, tin, aluminium and iron, but has included some of the rarer metals. Another study including several less common metals is that of Tarzwell and Henderson; most of their results are for bluegills[12].

Other investigators of the toxicity of metals to fish have not attempted general comparative studies but have limited their attention to single salts or to metals of one class. Schweiger[13] used salts of mercury, cadmium, nickel, cobalt and manganese, and found that their toxicity to the rainbow trout decreased in that order. Experiments were also made on carp and tench. The death of the fish was attributed to suffocation, caused by obstruction of the gills by mucous matter and 'cauterization' of the respiratory epithelium. Trama[14] studied the effect of a number of salts of sodium, potassium and calcium on the bluegill. Wiebe et al.[15] used golden shiners in a study of the chlorides of sodium, calcium and magnesium, and Garrey[2] used chlorides of sodium, calcium, magnesium and potassium in his study of the resistance of freshwater fish to changes in osmotic pressure.

Some of these salts, sodium chloride in particular, may be present in very high concentrations in certain effluents. Brine from oil wells is a major source of pollution in the south-western United States. A brine waste from an oil well studied by Clemens and Jones[16] had a total chloride content of 119,000 p.p.m.; the main cations were sodium, 59,700 p.p.m., calcium, 11,100 p.p.m. and magnesium, 2,070 p.p.m. Ten species of fish were used in tests with various dilutions of the neat effluent; the median toxicity thresholds ranged from 4·3 to 11·2 per cent of the original brine by volume. The test exposure period was 96 h. Fathead minnows and largemouth bass required the greatest dilution before they survived for this time. Clemens and Jones also carried out some threshold toxicity determinations with solutions of sodium chloride. These are given in Table 5.

Bandt[17] has studied the combined action of heavy metals on trout and roach. Copper and zinc, copper and cadmium, and nickel and zinc are stated to display synergism, whereas for cadmium and zinc, and nickel and cobalt the toxic effects are additive. Liepolt and Weber[18] have worked out survival curves for brown trout and minnows in copper sulphate solutions; tolerance limits for both fish are 0·4–1·0 p.p.m. Cu. Boetius[19] has studied the toxicity of mercuric chloride to rainbow trout and has shown that it is less toxic in seawater than in fresh water; his paper includes a discussion of whether the toxicity of mercuric chloride is changed by the formation of

Table 5. Lethal Limits for Metals as Salts*

Salt	Fish tested	Lethal concentration p.p.m.	Exposure time hours	Ref.
Aluminium nitrate .	stickleback	0·1 Al	144	3
Aluminium potassium sulphate (alum) . .	goldfish	100	12–96	7
Barium chloride .	,,	5,000	12–17	7
,, ,, .	salmon	158	?	20
Barium nitrate .	stickleback	500 Ba	180	3
Beryllium sulphate .	fathead minnow	0·2 Be	96	12
,, ,, .	bluegill	1·3 Be	96	12
Cadmium chloride .	goldfish	0·017	9–18	21
,, ,, .	fathead minnow	0·9	96	12
Cadmium (salt?) .	rainbow trout	3 Cd	168	13
Cadmium nitrate .	stickleback	0·3 Cd	190	3
Calcium nitrate .	goldfish	6,061	43–48	21
,, ,, .	stickleback	1,000 Ca	192	3
Cobalt chloride .	goldfish	10	168	7
Cobalt (salt?) .	rainbow trout	30 Co	168	13
Cobalt nitrate .	stickleback	15 Co	160	3
Copper nitrate .	salmon	0·18	?	20
,, ,, .	stickleback	0·02 Cu	192	25
,, ,, .	rainbow trout	0·08 Cu	20	22
Copper sulphate .	stickleback	0·03 Cu	160	3
,, ,, .	fathead minnow	0·05 Cu	96	12
,, ,, .	bluegill	0·2 Cu	96	12
,, ,, .	minnow	1·0 Cu	80	18
,, ,, .	brown trout	1·0 Cu	80	18
Cupric chloride .	goldfish	0·019	3–7	21
Lead chloride .	fathead minnow	2·4 Pb	96	12
Lead nitrate . .	minnow	0·33 Pb	?	23
,, ,, . .	stickleback	0·33 Pb	?	23
,, ,, . .	brown trout	0·33 Pb	?	23
,, ,, . .	stickleback	0·1 Pb	336	25
,, ,, . .	goldfish	10	1–2	25
,, ,, . .	rainbow trout	1 Pb	100	22
Magnesium nitrate .	stickleback	400 Mg	120	3
Manganese nitrate .	stickleback	50 Mn	160	3
Manganese (salt?) .	rainbow trout	75 Mn	168	13
Mercuric chloride .	,,	0·01 Hg	204	3
,, ,, .	rainbow trout	0·15 Hg	168	13
,, ,, .	,, ,,	1·0 Hg	600	19
Nickel chloride .	goldfish	10	200	7
,, ,, .	fathead minnow	4 Ni	96	12
Nickel nitrate .	stickleback	1 Ni	156	3
Nickel (salt?) .	rainbow trout	30 Ni	168	13

* In this table the concentration values are the lowest at which definite toxic action is indicated by the data in the reference cited. It must not be assumed that lower concentrations are harmless, and for further information the works cited should be consulted, as many include survival curves or tables. Most of the data are for temperatures between 15° and 23° C. Concentrations are parts per million. Exposure times have been approximated in some cases.

THE METALS AS SALTS

Table 5—cont.

Salt	Fish tested	Lethal concentration p.p.m.	Exposure time hours	Ref.
Potassium chloride .	goldfish	74·6	5–15	21
,, ,, .	straw-coloured minnow	373	12–29	2
Potassium nitrate .	stickleback	70 K	154	3
Silver nitrate	,,	0·004 Ag	180	3
Sodium chloride .	goldfish	10,000	240	7
,, ,, .	plains killifish	16,000	96	16
,, ,, .	green sunfish	10,713	96	16
,, ,, .	gambusia	10,670	96	16
,, ,, .	red shiner	9,513	96	16
,, ,, .	fathead minnow	8,718	96	16
,, ,, .	black bullhead	7,994	96	16
Sodium nitrate .	stickleback	600 Na	180	3
,, ,, .	goldfish	1,282	14	21
Sodium sulphite	,,	100	96	7
Strontium chloride .	,,	15,384	17–31	21
Strontium nitrate .	stickleback	1,500 Sr	164	3
Titanium sulphate .	fathead minnow	8·2 Ti	96	12
Uranyl sulphate .	,, ,,	2·8 U	96	12
Vanadyl sulphate .	,, ,,	4·8 V	96	12
,, ,, .	bluegill	6	96	12
Zinc sulphate	stickleback	0·3 Zn	204	25
,, ,, .	goldfish	100	120	7
,, ,, .	rainbow trout	0·5	64	24

double salts with sodium chloride. This is of some interest as mercury compounds are used in anti-fouling paints for ships.

A number of other papers dealing with the salts of the metals are discussed in the very comprehensive review of Doudoroff and Katz. Some of them, however, do not contribute much useful information as the duration of the tests is inadequate, and there are cases in which it does not seem clear as to whether the concentrations given are based on weights of anhydrous salt or salt with water of crystallization. Doudoroff and Katz consider that impurities in the chemicals used may account for some of the irregularities in the various results discussed. It is pointed out that in Oshima's experiments with eels, 0·65 p.p.m. of zinc was fatal more rapidly than 5,493 p.p.m. of manganese. Up to 0·01 per cent of zinc could be present in a sample of manganous salt which would meet American Chemical Society specification.

All data in the literature for threshold concentrations or tolerance limits must be applied with caution, for the extreme limits of toxicity, even at one specified temperature, have been determined for few substances and few fish. In considering the concentrations given as 48 h median tolerance limits it must be remembered that if the reaction follows the equation $C^n T = k$, n may have a value near unity, so that a concentration one-tenth of the 48 h tolerance limit may only permit a survival time of 20 days. If the reaction is represented by a curvilinear graph, following an equation of the form $(C-a)^n(T-b) = K$ the toxicity may fall off very rapidly below the 48 h limit. Table 5 gives some data for the metals as salts, gathered from the literature. Whenever possible all the data in the papers referred to should be studied; the survival periods given for different dilutions can help in the estimation of whether the fish may survive intermittent or occasional pollution.

The reactions of fish to solutions of metallic salts

In a paper published in 1912 Léger[26] reasoned that pollution which does not prove harmful within 1 h is negligible, because of the dilution that occurs thereafter in flowing streams, and because fish that are not overcome quickly can escape from the polluted water. The first experiments to test whether fish can recognize the presence of salts in solution were made by Wells[27], a few years later, with the gradient tank described in Chapter 3. Wells used the chlorides, nitrates and sulphates of ammonium, calcium and magnesium; his experiments were not very successful because the solutions, being of a higher specific gravity than the water, tended to stream along the bottom of the tank, and produced vertical as well as horizontal gradients. This trouble does not occur with an apparatus of the type used by the writer to test the reactions of fish to low concentrations of oxygen; a very sharp separation of water and solution can be obtained quite easily, except when the solution employed is highly concentrated, in which case it may be necessary to run in both water and solution at an increased rate. The reaction tube apparatus has been used by the writer to examine the extent to which fish can detect and avoid toxic concentrations of metallic salts[28, 29].

The first experiments were carried out with twelve-spined sticklebacks which, at the time, could be obtained more easily than the three-spined. They behaved very well in the apparatus, moving, generally, in an orderly fashion, and five fish could be used at a time, their positions being spotted on the chart at half-minute or minute intervals. The results shown in *Figure 31* are for 0·04, 0·003, 0·0003 and 0·0001 N zinc sulphate; approximately 1,300, 98, 9·8 and 3·3 p.p.m. zinc. Each experiment is begun with water running through both halves of the tube; after a few minutes, at the time indicated by the arrow, the zinc solution is run in on one side, so that in the centre of the tube the fish are presented with an abrupt transition from water to solution or solution to water according to their direction of movement.

A prompt negative reaction is seen at the highest concentration; occasionally a fish enters the salt zone where it swims in great agitation until it reaches the water-solution junction; here, after a moment's hesitation, it proceeds into the water. A negative reaction is also seen at 0·003 N, but it is less prompt; the solution does not appear to irritate the fish, which move very calmly. It will be noticed that there is some improvement in the reaction after the reversals of flow at 32 and 54 min. At 0·0003 N the movements of the fish are very leisurely and it takes several minutes for them to develop a definite preference for the water. At this concentration zinc sulphate appears

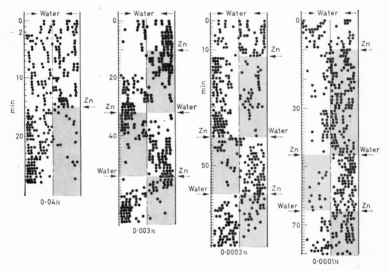

Figure 31. The reactions of groups of five sticklebacks to 0·04, 0·003, 0·0003 and 0·0001 N zinc sulphate. pH of solutions 6·2–6·6. Temperature 15° C. Survival times at these concentrations, in survival time experiments, 85 min, 190 min, 7 h, 15 h

(By courtesy of the Journal of Experimental Biology.)

to have no taste, even when held in the mouth for some time. No reaction developed in the 0·0001 N experiment, but the survival time at this concentration is about 15 h, and it is possible that the fish would shun the solution if given sufficient time. At the end of each experiment the fish were transferred to aquaria and all survived.

Experiments were also carried out to find whether the sticklebacks could recognize and select water after a period of immersion in zinc sulphate solution. In the first 0·01 N $ZnSO_4$ was run in at both ends of the apparatus for 18 min, in the second for 36 min. Water was then admitted on one side. In both cases the fish congregated in the water and avoided the solution almost immediately. In the second experiment the toxic process was well advanced, for marked respiratory distress had become evident.

Mercuric chloride solutions of concentration 300, 100, 30 and 4 p.p.m. Hg gave results similar in most respects to those obtained with zinc, but the ability of the fish to avoid the solutions was imperfect, and many died within 24 h, in the aquaria to which they were transferred at the end of the experiment. It should be noted, however, that the solutions used were highly toxic; the survival time at 4 p.p.m. Hg is only 100 min.

Experiments were carried out with copper sulphate over the concentration range 0·1–0·001 N, about 3,200–32 p.p.m. The first trials

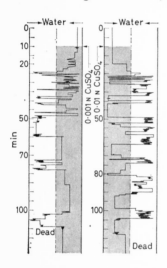

Figure 32.   The reactions of sticklebacks to 0·001 and 0·01 N copper sulphate.   Temperature 15° C

(By courtesy of the *Journal of Experimental Biology*.)

were made with groups of five fish and it was found that a vague negative reaction developed at 0·1 and 0·004 N, but at 0·01 N and at greater dilutions the fish displayed a 'positive' reaction, congregating in the solution end of the apparatus. The explanation of this curious positive reaction was forthcoming when further experiments were run at 0·01–0·001 N with single fish, whose behaviour was carefully watched. Two typical records are shown in *Figure 32*. The fish seem to be totally incapable of recognizing the solution and swim across the water–copper sulphate junction in either direction without the slightest hesitation. In the solution they seem to become stupefied and rest on the bottom; after short periods, shown by the vertical traces in *Figure 32*, they seem to revive a little and swim into the water; this seems to stimulate them to random movement which generally lands them back in the solution, where they spend another period of stupor. The 'positive' result therefore is not due to the fish selecting the solution. The whole explanation lies in the fact that they cannot perceive the toxic substance so that it acts as a trap. A somewhat similar effect is seen when a drop of dilute HCl is introduced into a culture of the protozoan *Paramecium*. They appear to be attracted by the acid as a dense aggregation is formed around the drop; the explanation is that the drop of acid forms a trap into which the organisms swim, to be killed or paralysed[30].

Using *Gasterosteus*, the three-spined stickleback, as test animal the effect of lead nitrate solutions was studied over the concentration range 0·00001–0·1 N, equivalent to about 1–10,000 p.p.m. Pb. Four typical results are given in *Figure 33*. At the highest concentrations the fish display a preference for the solution, but at concentrations

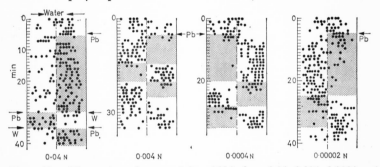

Figure 33. The reactions of groups of five sticklebacks to 0·04, 0·004, 0·0004 and 0·00002 N lead nitrate (approximately 4,000, 400, 40 and 2 p.p.m.). Temperature 14° C. pH of solutions 5·4, 5·8, 6·4, 6·8. Survival times 3, 4, 5½, 16 h

(By courtesy of the *Journal of Experimental Biology*.)

below 400 p.p.m. a good avoiding reaction is seen. On running in the solution the fish are greatly agitated and quickly choose the water zone. Here they remain and should one of them venture to the centre of the tube it pauses, gobbles and retreats. Even at 2 p.p.m. Pb a delayed, but quite definite, negative reaction is seen; at 1 p.p.m. it may take about 30 min to develop. The survival time at 2 p.p.m. is about 16 h and at 1 p.p.m. 19–20 h. Experiments were later carried out with minnows (*Phoxinus phoxinus*) and these showed an even greater ability to detect and avoid lead nitrate solutions; a 10 p.p.m. solution was avoided immediately and even a 0·4 p.p.m. solution was rejected after about 8 min. Small trout also react negatively to lead nitrate; in the record shown in *Figure 34* it will be noted that the fish 'tested' the solution four times between 7 and 10 min, and stayed in the water. Moncrieff[31] supplies some information on the sensitivity of the human sense of taste to heavy metal salts, stating that silver nitrate is just detectable in 0·003 per cent solution; this would be about 19 p.p.m. Ag.

These experiments show that the capacity of fish to detect and avoid toxic concentrations of metallic salts varies very much with different species, and that the same species may exhibit, to different salts, an extreme variety of sensitivity. There seems to be no relation

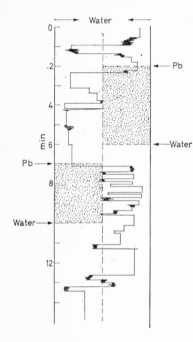

Figure 34. Record of the reactions of a small trout to 0·0001 N *lead nitrate. Temperature* 18° C

between the toxicity of salts and the type of reaction displayed. The four heavy metals tested, in order of decreasing toxicity, form the series mercuric chloride, copper sulphate, lead nitrate, zinc sulphate. According to the stickleback's ability to detect and avoid them the order is lead, mercury, zinc, copper.

REFERENCES

[1] Bert, M. P. Sur les phénomènes et les causes de la mort des animaux d'eau douce que l'on plonge dans l'eau de mer. *C.R. Acad. Sci., Paris,* 73 (1871) 382–5, 464–7
[2] Garrey, W. C. The resistance of fresh water fish to changes of osmotic and chemical conditions. *Amer. J. Physiol.,* 39 (1916) 313–29

THE METALS AS SALTS

3 Jones, J. R. E.   The relation between the electrolytic solution pressures of the metals and their toxicity to the stickleback (*Gasterosteus aculeatus* L.). *J. exp. Biol.*, 16 (1939) 425–37

4 Klein, L.   *Aspects of River Pollution.* 1957.   London; Butterworths

5 Goodman, L. S. and Gilman, A.   *The Pharmacological Basis of Therapeutics*, 2nd edn.   1955.   New York; Macmillan

6 Smith, H. W.   The absorption and excretion of water and salts by marine teleosts.   *Amer. J. Physiol.*, 93 (1930) 480–505

7 Ellis, M. M.   Detection and measurement of stream pollution.   *Bull. U.S. Bur. Fish.*, 48 (1937) 365–437

8 Richet, C.   De l'action chimique des différents métaux sur le coeur de la grenouille.   *C.R. Acad. Sci.*, Paris, 94 (1882) 742–4

9 Mathews, A. P.   The relation between solution tension, atomic volume and physiological action of the elements.   *Amer. J. Physiol.*, 10 (1904) 290–323

10 Glasstone, S.   *Text Book of Physical Chemistry*, 2nd edn.   1960.   London; Macmillan

11 Doudoroff, P. and Katz, M.   Critical review of literature on the toxicity of industrial wastes and their components to fish.   II. The metals as salts.   *Sewage industr. Wastes*, 25 (1953) 802–39

12 Tarzwell, C. M. and Henderson, C.   Toxicity of less common metals to fishes.   *Industr. Wastes*, 5 (1960) 12

13 Schweiger, G.   Die toxicologische Einwirkung von Schwermetallsalzen auf Fische und Fischnährtiere.   *Arch. Fischereiwissenschaft*, 8 (1957) 54–78

14 Trama, F. B.   The acute toxicity of some common salts of sodium, potassium and calcium to the common bluegill (*Lepomis macrochirus* Rafinesque).   *Proc. nat. Acad. Sci. Phil.*, 106 (1954) 185–214

15 Wiebe, A. H., Burr, J. G. and Faubion, H. E.   The problem of stream pollution in Texas with special reference to salt water from oil fields.   *Trans. Amer. Fish. Soc.*, 64 (1934) 81–6

16 Clemens, H. P. and Jones, W. H.   Toxicity of brine water from oil wells.   *Trans. Amer. Fish. Soc.*, 84 (1954) 97–109

17 Bandt, H. J.   Ueber verstärkte Schadwirkung auf Fische insbesondere über erhöhte Giftwirkung durch Kombination von Abwassergiften.   *Beitr. WasserChem.*, 1 (1946) 15–23

18 Liepolt, R. and Weber, E.   Die Giftwirkung von Kupfersulfat auf Wasserorganismen.   *Wass. u. Abwass.* (1958) 335–53

19 Boetius, J.   Lethal action of mercuric chloride and phenylmercuric acetate on fishes.   *Medd. Danm. Fiskeri- og Havunders*, n.s., 3 (1960–61) 93–115

20 *State of Washington 64th Ann. Rep. Fish.*, 1944

21 Powers, E. B.   The goldfish (*Carassius carassius*) as a test animal in the study of toxicity.   *Illinois biol. Monogr.*, 4 (1917) 127–93

22 *Water Pollution Research, 1959.*   1960.   London; H.M.S.O.

23 Carpenter, K. E.   The lethal action of soluble metallic salts on fishes.   *Brit. J. exp. Biol.*, 4 (1927) 378–90

24 Lloyd, R.   The toxicity of zinc sulphate to rainbow trout.   *Ann. appl. Biol.*, 48 (1960) 84–94

25 Jones, J. R. E.   The relative toxicity of salts of lead, zinc and copper to the stickleback (*Gasterosteus aculeatus* L.) and the effect of calcium on the toxicity of lead and zinc salts.   *J. exp. Biol.*, 15 (1938) 394–407

[26] Léger, L. Études sur l'action nocive des produits de déversements industriels chemiques dans les eaux douces, 2e ser. Eaux de décapage des métaux. *Ann. Univ. Grenoble*, 24 (1912) 41–122

[27] Wells, M. M. The reactions and resistance of fishes in their natural environment to salts. *J. exp. Zool.*, 19 (1915) 248–83

[28] Jones, J. R. E. The reactions of *Pygosteus pungitius* L. to toxic solutions. *J. exp. Biol.*, 24 (1947) 110–22

[29] Jones, J. R. E. A further study of the reactions of fish to toxic solutions. *J. exp. Biol.*, 25 (1948) 22–34

[30] Loeb, J. *Forced Movements, Tropisms and Animal Conduct.* 1912. Philadelphia; J. B. Lippincott

[31] Moncrieff, R. W. *The Chemical Senses.* 1944. London; Leonard Hill

7

THE RESPIRATORY DEPRESSANTS: CYANIDES AND SULPHIDES

HYDROCYANIC acid or hydrogen cyanide, HCN, was discovered in 1782 by Scheele who prepared it by heating prussian blue with sulphuric acid, hence its name, prussic acid. Its salts, the cyanides, are now very important industrial chemicals used for case-hardening, metal cleaning, electroplating and the preparation of fumigants for insect control. The acid and its salts are extremely poisonous—the pure acid must be one of the most poisonous of all inorganic substances. The famous French physiologist Claude Bernard observed that when animals were poisoned by hydrocyanic acid the venous blood became bright red, like the oxygen-saturated blood in the arteries, suggesting that the tissues had lost their capacity for taking up oxygen; this was in 1857. Some years later Geppert[1] showed that this explanation was correct; when animals were given a small, sublethal dose, they consumed less oxygen and produced correspondingly less carbon dioxide. When Krogh[2] wrote his book on the respiratory exchange of animals and man it was known that cyanides seemed to depress respiration in living tissues of all types, and that they had no effect on the combination of oxygen with haemoglobin so that transport of oxygen by the blood was not affected. About this time physiologists were searching for the respiratory enzyme or 'Atmungsferment'; such a substance was detected in the thoracic muscles of bees in 1886, but it was not isolated. Keilin[3] rediscovered it in 1925 and named it 'cytochrome'. This is now known to be a mixture of several distinct components forming a complex system of oxygen carriers and catalysts. The cytochrome system is inactivated by hydrocyanic acid, so that the tissues become incapable of utilizing the oxygen brought to them by the blood. In the higher animals very small doses may act as a respiratory stimulant[4] but any considerable dose is a respiratory depressant, and large doses, acting rapidly to paralyse the central nervous system, arrest the respiratory movements, the beating of the heart and other vital functions.

Powers[5] appears to have been the first to test the toxicity of cyanides to fish. Using potassium cyanide and the goldfish he obtained a survival curve of much the same general nature as that given by the other substances he tested. The reciprocals of the times, plotted against the concentrations on linear scales, formed a sigmoid 'fatality curve' whose straight central portion, when produced, cut the concentration axis. Alexander, Southgate and Bassindale[6], who found that cyanide was one of the chief poisonous substances in effluents discharged into the estuary of the River Tees, studied the effect of potassium cyanide solutions on salmon smolts and rainbow trout. Their sensitivity proved to be of much the same order. In the solutions the fish remained very quiet; sooner or later, according to the concentration, they suddenly lost their equilibrium, and then could not regain their normal swimming position—they took up a

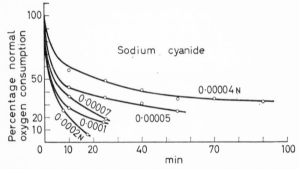

Figure 35. The effect of five different concentrations of sodium cyanide on the oxygen consumption of the stickleback. In each experiment 10 small fish were placed in the respiration chamber. The pH of each solution was adjusted to 7·0 by adding sufficient hydrochloric acid. Temperature 17° C

(By courtesy of the *Journal of Experimental Biology.*)

vertical position, head uppermost, with the gill covers widely distended. Left in this state the fish died within a short time but they would recover if taken out of the solution and placed in clean water immediately after overturning. The toxicity of the cyanide solutions was found to increase rapidly with a rise in temperature; over the temperature range 6–19° C the toxicity of a solution containing 3 p.p.m. CN was more than doubled.

Alexander, Southgate and Bassindale have drawn a toxicity-concentration curve for the rainbow trout in potassium cyanide solutions at 5–7° C. The concentrations and the reciprocals of the survival times are plotted on linear scales. The concentration range studied is small, from 0·42 to 0·13 p.p.m. CN, and the graph seems to indicate a threshold of toxicity in the region of 0·1 p.p.m. CN. It was noticed that the gills of fish dying in the cyanide solutions became much brighter than the gills of normal fish; this is due to the changes in the condition of the arterial blood brought about by the inactivation of the respiratory enzymes. This gill colour brightening is an important symptom of fish dying from cyanide poisoning. The effects on gill colour of a number of other toxic substances present in effluents discharged into the Tees estuary were also examined; *p*-cresol, naphthalene and spent still liquor produced a darkening, and a similar result was seen with water deficient in dissolved oxygen, as might be expected.

The effect of cyanide solutions on the respiration of fish is illustrated by *Figure 35*, which shows the effect of five different concentrations of sodium cyanide on the oxygen consumption of the stickleback[7]. The critical concentration for *Gasterosteus* at 17° C is about 0·00004 N or 1 p.p.m. CN, which brings the respiration rate down to about 32 per cent of normal in 90 min. At lower concentrations the fish will survive for a very long time in a condition resembling anaesthesia; they lie on their sides, making no attempts to swim and breathing very slowly. Chloroform is another substance which reduces the respiration rate of fish, and it is interesting to find that here again the critical stage seems to be reached, with the stickleback, when the oxygen intake is reduced to about one-third of the normal value. This occurs when the solution contains 140 p.p.m. of chloroform; at first the fish struggles furiously, later it becomes quiet, sinking to the bottom of the experiment chamber. Here it rests, almost rigid, propped on its tail and pelvic spines. Its eyes are set in a fixed stare and the respiratory movements are of enormous amplitude, the gill covers heaving up and down about 30 times per min. Cyanide solutions of concentrations appreciably higher than 1 p.p.m. are fatal, because there is a tendency to sudden failure of the respiratory movements.

A more complete picture of the changes in respiration rate exhibited by a stickleback in a cyanide solution is given by *Figure 36*, where both the oxygen consumption and the opercular movement rate for the fish are recorded. It will be seen that after a brief period of greatly increased frequency the opercular movement rate declines roughly in step with the oxygen consumption. On replacing the cyanide solution by water at 30 min a recovery begins; the fish begins to breathe more quickly and consumes more oxygen. Soon it regains its sense of balance and swims around normally. In about an hour from the time at which the toxic process is interrupted the respiration rate is back to normal. On referring to *Figure 27* it will be seen that here the recovery process is much slower, but in this case damage to the gill apparatus is involved; there is no evidence that this occurs with cyanides.

Recovery from cyanide poisoning is believed to come about by the conversion of cyanide to thiocyanate; this does not have the same inhibitory effect upon respiratory enzymes. Bodansky[8] has shown that in man the administration of small doses of potassium cyanide is followed by an increase in the thiocyanate content of the saliva. According to Williams[9] the conversion of cyanide to thiocyanate is an

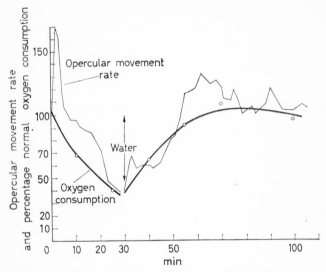

Figure 36. Oxygen consumption and opercular movement rate curves for a single stickleback in 0·00005 N NaCN, *showing recovery following the replacement of the cyanide solution by water at* 30 min. *Temperature* 17° C

(By courtesy of the *Journal of Experimental Biology.*)

enzymic process involving the enzyme rhodanese. This enzyme is specific for hydrogen cyanide which it converts into thiocyanic acid very quickly, in the presence of sodium thiosulphate or colloidal sulphur. Accordingly, thiosulphate is used as an antidote in cyanide poisoning. Achard and Binet[10] have shown that a 0·2 per cent solution of sodium thiosulphate will give carp a considerable measure of protection against 0·002 per cent of KCN.

It has been shown that the toxicity of hydrogen cyanide may be ascribed chiefly to the action of undissociated molecules of HCN, which are said to have a much greater power of penetrating living tissues than dissociated ions[11]. Sodium and potassium cyanide form hydrogen cyanide on solution in water; the extent of this hydrolysis $(KCN+H_2O=K^+ +OH^- +HCN)$ is greatly influenced by the pH of the solution, becoming greater by an increase in acidity, depressed by the addition of alkalis. It should follow that the toxicity of cyanides will vary with the pH of the solution and the experiments of Wuhrmann and Woker[12] are in agreement. They found that in a solution containing 0·66 p.p.m. CN the concentration of molecular HCN was 0·45 p.p.m. at pH 8·84. On bringing down the pH to 8·12 the molecular HCN increased to 0·62 p.p.m., and at pH 7·58 it reached 0·66 p.p.m. With the fall in pH there was an increase in toxicity; at the pH values 8·84, 8·12 and 7·58 the overturning times for chub (*Squalius cephalus*) were 94, 70 and 54 min.

Herbert and Merkens[13] and Herbert and Downing[14] have made a study of the toxicity of potassium cyanide solutions to rainbow trout, using large numbers of animals and a constant flow apparatus. Their work is mainly a very careful study of the relation between concentration and survival time and has been discussed in Chapter 4. They did not make any experiments to examine the pH–toxicity relationship; over the concentration range studied the pH varied from 7·4 to 8·0, and the data of Wuhrmann and Woker[12] show that in this pH range at least 93 per cent of the cyanide present would be in the form of undissociated HCN. Downing[15] has shown that a reduction in the oxygen content of the water increases the toxicity of cyanide solutions, but does not suggest any explanation for this. It might be thought that a reduction in the amount of oxygen available would make little difference if the animal cannot utilize it, but this argument would apply only if the cyanide inhibited oxidation completely. There is evidence that cyanide cannot bring about a complete suppression of protoplasmic oxidation, even at high concentrations, and it has been claimed that the respiratory enzyme system which can be inactivated by cyanide only accounts for about two-thirds of the oxidation going on in animal tissues, the remaining third being accounted for by a system stable to cyanide. Very different results have been obtained by different students of this problem; according to Commoner[16] the cyanide-sensitive enzyme system is most active in connection with the oxidation of carbohydrates; the cyanide-stable system has an activity which is relatively small and varies from organ to organ and from organism to organism.

The anaesthetic-like effect of cyanides upon fish is useful in pisciculture and sodium cyanide can be used to remove unwanted fish from ponds. Sufficient is added to the water to give a concentration of about 1 p.p.m. and the fish will begin to surface in 5–30 min.

Those to be kept alive can be removed and placed in fresh water, where they recover; the survival percentage is said to be excellent[17].

Wuhrmann[18] has worked out a number of survival curves for cyanide, the fish being the minnow, chub, perch and tench. His results differ from the rainbow trout data of Herbert and Merkens in that the log/log graphs are curved, conforming to equations of the type $(C-a)^n(T-b)=K$, discussed in Chapter 4. The curves indicate very similar thresholds of toxicity for the different species; all would appear to be in the range 0·1–0·2 p.p.m. The threshold reaction times, however, vary considerably; that for the perch seems to be about 4 min but the minimum survival time recorded for the tench is over 30 min at a concentration of 100 p.p.m. CN. Wuhrmann has also studied the effect of temperature on the toxicity of cyanide to the tench, the minnow and the trout. At 0·5 p.p.m. CN raising the temperature from 5° C to 20° C brings the survival time for the trout from 8 min down to 3 min, the survival time for the minnow falls from 50 min to about 12 min; that for the tench from 270 to 90 min. A comparative study of the effect of cyanides on some American fish has been made by Renn[19] using a constant flow, constant concentration apparatus.

Doudoroff[20] has studied the toxicity of sodium cyanide to fathead minnows and has shown that these fish are rather more resistant than trout, their median tolerance limit at 20° C being 0·23 p.p.m. for 96 h. The toxicity of complex cyanides was also examined. With sodium cyanide, zinc sulphate forms a complex which is very toxic, the tolerance limit expressed as p.p.m. of total cyanide being only 0·18 for 96 h. Cadmium sulphate also forms a very toxic complex with sodium cyanide. With nickel sulphate, however, a complex is formed which is markedly less toxic than the compounds producing it; interest in the nickel cyanide complex has been stimulated by the publication of a paper by Milne[21] wherein combination with nickel was proposed as a practical method of detoxification of cyanide wastes.

Doudoroff found that the nickelocyanide complex is formed on mixing sodium cyanide and nickel sulphate so that the weight ratio of nickel to cyanide in the solution is 0·57. The Ni/CN ratio for $Ni(CN)_4^=$ is 0·56. The effect of solutions of this composition on fathead minnows was tested and it was found that their toxicity was increased by the presence of the test fish. Frequently renewed solutions were relatively harmless; solutions in which a number of minnows had been kept until they died were soon fatal to a new batch of fish. This rise in toxicity was shown to follow the fall in pH brought about by the production of carbon dioxide by the test animals. Further experiments with solutions of varying degree of alkalinity showed that the nickelocyanide complex is relatively harmless when the pH is 8·0 or higher. In less alkaline or acid solutions the complex tends to dissociate, with the formation of hydrogen cyanide.

A summary of the available data for the tolerance of fish to cyanide solutions is given in Table 6 (p. 94). Southgate[22] considers that the safe concentration for cyanide is much lower than most of the figures quoted. He suggests that in waters where fish are expected to live for long periods the amount of cyanide present should not be allowed to exceed 0·01 p.p.m. Until further information is available about the tolerance of fish to cyanide and the extent to which they can become acclimatized to it, this would appear to be a good standard at which to aim. Whether fish can detect the presence of cyanide in solution does not appear to have been tested.

In man, hydrogen sulphide acts as a respiratory depressant and a local irritant, producing conjunctivitis, bronchial irritation and oedema of the lungs. When sulphide solutions are added to freshly drawn blood the oxyhaemoglobin is reduced immediately and the blood takes on a dark, venous colour. At the same time a greenish compound of sulphide and haemoglobin is formed, but these changes only occur when the available concentration of sulphide in the blood is very high[24]; lower concentrations appear to have a toxic action similar to that of cyanide, a tissue anoxia resulting from the inactivation of respiratory enzymes[4]. Sulphide is oxidized to the comparatively innocuous sulphate in the body so that recovery may take place if the dose is not too great. As in the case of cyanide there is evidence that undissociated molecules of the compound penetrate living tissues more readily than dissociated ions. In experiments to measure the rate of penetration of hydrogen sulphide into cells of the alga *Valonia* it has been shown that the rate of penetration is proportional to the concentration of molecular H_2S in the external solution[25]. Shelford[26] was one of the first to draw attention to the importance of sulphides as polluting substances. He pointed out that they occurred in gas wastes, and were produced by the decomposition of sewage and other organic matter in water. He tested the effect of solutions of hydrogen sulphide on fish and found that 2 cm^3/l. was fatal. Shelford also studied the reactions of fish to sulphide solutions with the gradient tank and found that they would avoid 'strong concentrations' but would be attracted into weak solutions.

Longwell and Pentelow[27], in a study of the effect of fresh and septic sewage on trout, found that a substance appeared to be present which was volatile in acid solution and directly toxic to the fish. Sulphides were present in the sewage samples in fair concentrations, especially the septic samples. The effect of sodium sulphide solutions on trout was tested and it was found that the toxicity was very dependent on the pH (*Figure 37*); the overturning time increased with an increase in alkalinity, decreased on the acid side, was reasonably constant between pH 6·9 and 7·6. This effect is evidently due to the changes in the degree of hydrolysis of the sodium sulphide, the addition of acid tending to increase the proportion of molecular H_2S present. The survival and fatality curves show that the toxic effect is maintained below 1 p.p.m. S; the linear portion of the fatality curve indicates a threshold concentration at about 0·05 p.p.m. S. It is evident that

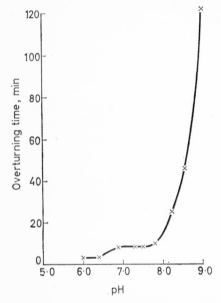

Figure 37. The effect of pH *changes on the toxicity of a solution of sodium sulphide (3·2 p.p.m. S) to the trout*

(From Longwell and Pentelow[27], by courtesy of the *Journal of Experimental Biology.*)

when rivers are polluted by sewage the concentration of hydrogen sulphide must be taken into account, as well as the oxygen content. In septic sewage, sulphides are produced by the action of anaerobic organisms on sulphates and organic sulphur compounds. In well-aerated water hydrogen sulphide is slowly oxidized, forming colloidal sulphur.

Belding[28] studied the effect of hydrogen sulphide on the respiratory movements of fish. He found that at 3·2, 6·3, 12·7 and 25·3 p.p.m. the breathing rate of carp is slowed down when the fish are placed in the solution, and the respiratory movements may stop. Later the breathing movements restart or speed up, but they do not return to normal and after a time they slow down and stop, and the fish dies (*Figure 38*). Belding made no measurements of the oxygen consump-

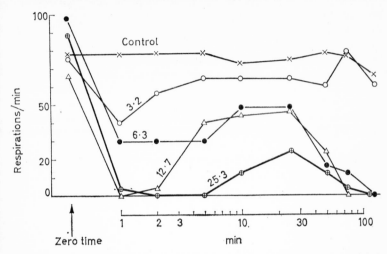

Figure 38.   The effect of 3·2, 6·3, 12·7 *and* 25·3 p.p.m. *solutions of hydrogen sulphide on the breathing rate of carp*

(Drawn from the data of Belding[28].)

tion.   The writer's experiments with sticklebacks[7] show that for solutions of pH 7·0 in soft water the critical concentration is about 0·0002 N or 3·2 p.p.m. S; this will depress the oxygen consumption to about 33 per cent of normal in 90 min (*Figure 39*).   More dilute

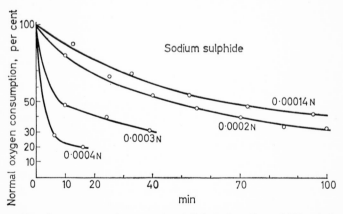

Figure 39.   Oxygen consumption curves for sticklebacks in sodium sulphide solutions at 17° C.   *In each experiment three were placed in the respiration fish flask.   The* pH *of the solutions was adjusted to* 7·0 *by the addition of sufficient sulphuric acid*

(By courtesy of the *Journal of Experimental Biology*.)

91

solutions are tolerated for rapidly increasing times; high concentrations are quickly fatal. Thus a stickleback placed in a 16 p.p.m. solution loses its sense of balance almost at once and ceases breathing in about 6 min. As in the case of cyanide the opercular movement rate falls with the oxygen consumption and fish exhibit a remarkable power of recovery provided that they are removed from the solution before they cease breathing. The record of an experiment with a stickleback in 0·00035 N Na_2S solution is given in *Figure 40*. The

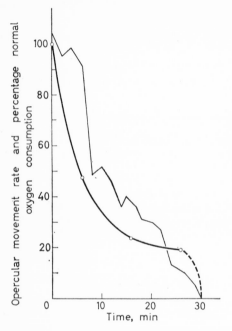

Figure 40.   Oxygen consumption (heavy) and opercular movement rate (light) curves for a stickleback in 0·00035 N sodium sulphide. Temperature 17° C

(By courtesy of the *Journal of Experimental Biology*.)

·lethal limit for the stickleback is rather less than 2·4 p.p.m. H_2S. The limit for the trout according to Stroede[29] is 1 p.p.m., his figure for the carp and tench is 8–12 p.p.m.

It is well known that the human olfactory organs can detect hydrogen sulphide at great dilution. A 1/100,000 mixture is most unpleasant and Moncrieff[30] states that a 1/10,000,000 mixture of H_2S and air is detectable. No information appears to be available on the capability of the human organs of smell and taste for detecting the gas in solution. The ability of sticklebacks to detect and avoid solutions of sodium sulphide has been tested with the reaction tube apparatus[31] and a representative series of the results obtained is shown in *Figure 41*. At 0·0007 N (11 p.p.m.) the fish display much distress immediately the solution is admitted and swim actively until all have gathered in the water zone; thereafter they avoid the solution in a most definite fashion and assemble very quickly on the other side of the apparatus if the directions of flow of water and solution are reversed. At lower concentrations the fish take a somewhat longer time to react and at 0·00008 N or 1·3 p.p.m. S a definite preference for the water is not established until they have been exposed to the sulphide solution for about 45 min. The 'reaction times', the times for which the solution must be present before all of five fish select the water zone and will not voluntarily enter the solution, were determined for nine sulphide solutions covering the concentration

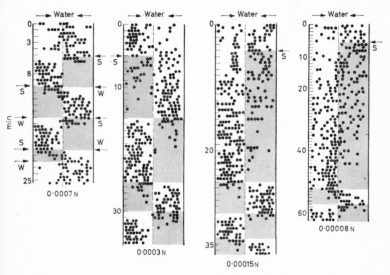

Figure 41. The reactions of groups of five sticklebacks to 0·0007, 0·0003, 0·00015 and 0·00008 N sodium sulphide. Temperature 14° C. pH of solutions 6·8

(By courtesy of the *Journal of Experimental Biology*.)

range 0·0001–0·001 N Na$_2$S or 1·6–16 p.p.m. S. These times are plotted in *Figure 42* together with the survival times. It will be seen that the reaction times are very much shorter than the survival times, so that if sticklebacks encounter a toxic concentration of sulphide there is a reasonable chance that they will be repelled by it before they are harmed. If this holds for other fish it would explain why they are not usually killed by sewage polluted water if escape is possible. It may explain why fish are often absent below the outfalls of organic effluents even though the oxygen content of the water remains well above their lower limit of tolerance[32, 33].

93

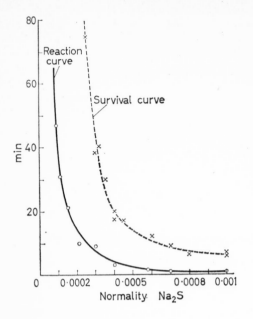

Figure 42. Survival and reaction time curves for the stickleback in sodium sulphide solutions. Temperature 14° C

(By courtesy of the *Journal of Experimental Biology*.)

Table 6. Lethal Limits for Cyanides*

Fish		*Temp.* °C	*Exposure time* hours	p.p.m. CN	*Ref.*
Rainbow trout	.	5–7	?	0·1	6
Stickleback	.	17	2–3	0·8	7
Rainbow trout	.	17·5	74	0·07	13
Minnow	.	15	10	0·10	18
Perch	.	15	17	0·13	18
Tench	.	15	48	0·2	18
Chub	.	15	48	0·22	18
White crappie	.	25	24	0·045	19
Yellowbelly	.	25	24	0·078	19
Bluegill	.	25	24	0·091	19
Largemouth bass	.	25	24	0·11	19
Fathead minnow	.	20	96	0·23	20
Speckled trout	.	?	120	0·05	23

* The concentrations given in column 4 are the lowest at which definite toxicity is indicated by the data in the reference cited. In most cases the tests were conducted with solutions of sodium or potassium cyanide. Some concentration values are approximate as they are read from survival curves.

RESPIRATORY DEPRESSANTS: CYANIDES AND SULPHIDES

REFERENCES

[1] Geppert, J. Über das Wesen der Blausäurevergiftung. *Z. f. klin. Med.*, 15 (1889) 208–43, 307–69

[2] Krogh, A. *The Respiratory Exchange of Animals and Man.* 1916. London; Longmans, Green

[3] Keilin, D. On cytochrome, a respiratory pigment, common to animals, yeast and higher plants. *Proc. roy. Soc., B.* 98 (1925) 312–39

[4] Goodman, L. S. and Gilman, A. *The Pharmacological Basis of Therapeutics*, 2nd edn. 1955 New York; Macmillan

[5] Powers, E. B. The goldfish (*Carassius carassius*) as a test animal in the study of toxicity. *Illinois biol. Monogr.*, 4 (1917) 127–93

[6] Alexander, W. B., Southgate, B. A. and Bassindale, R. Survey of the River Tees. Pt. II. The Estuary—Chemical and Biological. *Tech. Pap. Wat. Pollut. Res., Lond.*, No. 5 (1935)

[7] Jones, J. R. E. The oxygen consumption of *Gasterosteus aculeatus* L. in toxic solutions. *J. exp. Biol.* 23 (1947) 298–311

[8] Bodansky, M. The conversion of cyanide into thiocyanate in man and in alkaline solutions of cystine. *J. Pharmacol. exp. Therap.*, 37 (1929) 463–74

[9] Williams, R. T. *Detoxication Mechanisms.* 1949. London; Chapman and Hall

[10] Achard C. and Binet, L. Les effets de l'hyposulfite de soude sur l'intoxication par le cyanure de potassium. *C.R. Acad. Sci. Paris*, 198 (1934) 222–4

[11] Brinley, F. J. Studies on the physiological effects of hydrogen cyanide. *Biol. Bull., Wood's Hole*, 53 (1927) 365–89

[12] Wuhrmann, K. and Woker, H. Experimentelle Untersuchungen über die Ammoniak- und Blausäurevergiftung. *Schweiz. Z. Hydrol.*, 11 (1948) 210–44

[13] Herbert, D. W. M. and Merkens, J. C. The toxicity of potassium cyanide to trout. *J. exp. Biol.*, 29 (1952) 632–49

[14] Herbert, D. W. M. and Downing, K. M. A further study of the toxicity of potassium cyanide to rainbow trout (*Salmo gairdnerii* Richardson). *Ann. appl. Biol.*, 43 (1955) 237–42

[15] Downing, K. M. The influence of dissolved oxygen concentration on the toxicity of potassium cyanide to trout. *J. exp. Biol.*, 31 (1954) 161–4

[16] Commoner, B. Cyanide inhibition as a means of elucidating the mechanisms of cellular respiration. *Biol. Rev.*, 15 (1940) 168–201

[17] Bridges, W. R. Sodium cyanide as a fish poison. *Fish. Bull., U.S.*, 253 (1958) 1–11

[18] Wuhrmann, K. Sur quelques principes de la toxicologie du poisson. *Bull. du C.B.E.D.E.*, 15 (1952) 49–60

[19] Renn, C. E. Biological properties and behaviours of cyanogenic wastes. *Sewage industr. Wastes*, 27 (1955) 297–310

[20] Doudoroff, P. Some experiments on the toxicity of complex cyanides to fish. *Sewage industr. Wastes*, 28 (1956) 1020–40

[21] Milne, D. Disposal of cyanides by complexation. *Sewage industr. Wastes*, 22 (1950) 1192

[22] Southgate, B. A. Treatment in Great Britain of industrial waste waters containing cyanides. *Water Sanit. Engr.*, 4 (1953) 213–17

[23] Karsten, A. Effect of cyanide on Black Hills trout. *Black Hills Eng.*, 22 (1934) 145–74

95

[24] Edmunds, C. W. and Gunn, J. A.   11th edn of *Cushny's Text-book of Pharmacology and Therapeutics*.   1936.   London; Churchill

[25] Jacques, A. G.   The kinetics of penetration, XII. Hydrogen sulphide. *J. gen. Physiol.*, 19 (1936) 397–418

[26] Shelford, V. E.   An experimental study of the effects of gas wastes upon fishes, with especial reference to stream pollution.   *Bull. Ill. Lab. nat. Hist.*, 11 (1917) 381–412

[27] Longwell, J. and Pentelow, F. T. K.   The effect of sewage on brown trout (*Salmo trutta* L.).   *J. exp. Biol.*, 12 (1935) 1–12

[28] Belding, D. L.   The respiratory movements of fish as an indicator of a toxic environment.   *Trans. Amer. Fish. Soc.*, 59 (1929) 238–45

[29] Stroede, W.   Schwefelwasserstoff und Sauerstoff in unseren natürlichen Gewässern.   *Z. Fisch.*, 31 (1933) 345–51

[30] Moncrieff, R. W.   *The Chemical Senses*.   1944.   London; Leonard Hill

[31] Jones, J. R. E.   A further study of the reactions of fish to toxic solutions. *J. exp. Biol.*, 25 (1948) 22–34

[32] Rasmussen, C. J.   On the effect of silage juice in Danish streams.   *Verh. int. Ver. Limnol.*, 12 (1955) 819–22

[33] Pentelow, F. T. K., Butcher, R. W. and Grindley, J.   An investigation of the effects of milk wastes on the Bristol Avon.   *Min. Ag. Fish., Fish. Invest.*, Ser. I. 4 (1938) No. 1, 80 pp.

8

THE INORGANIC GASES

THERE is a considerable literature dealing with the effects of carbon dioxide on fish. The work published prior to 1950 has been reviewed by Doudoroff and Katz[1] who have pointed out the unsatisfactory nature of much of the available data. Very few experiments designed to test the resistance of fish to abnormal concentrations of carbon dioxide have covered adequate exposure times; in other experiments, respiratory distress and other symptoms developed after a sudden change in the carbon dioxide concentration and pH, seem to have been taken to indicate a harmful effect, little attempt being made to see whether the animal could adjust itself to the new conditions.

The effects of carbon dioxide on man are well understood and are described in the textbooks of human physiology. The gas is a vital factor in the regulation of the breathing rate and acts as a respiratory stimulant when present in the air breathed in concentrations of 2–3 per cent. The normal amount present in the atmosphere is 0·04 per cent and increasing this to 2 per cent will step up the alveolar ventilation in man by as much as 50 per cent, even when there is no diminution in the amount of oxygen available. It would appear that the pulmonary ventilation is so controlled as to react to the slightest change in the CO_2 tension in the blood; any increase in this is followed by a compensatory increase in ventilation, so that the alveolar CO_2 concentration is maintained at the normal level of 5·5 per cent, or very nearly. When there is an unusually high concentration of CO_2 in the air breathed the alveolar concentration never falls completely back to normal, for should it do so the stimulus to more energetic breathing would cease and CO_2 would reaccumulate[2]. The compensatory mechanism has its limits, and when the amount present in the air breathed exceeds 6 per cent the gas begins to accumulate in the blood in spite of the increase in the rate and depth of the respiratory movements. Marked toxic effects may then appear, the central nervous system is depressed, the heartbeat is slowed down and the subject may become unconscious. Later the respiratory movements may cease.

Whether the gas acts as a respiratory stimulant in fish is uncertain as the available evidence seems to be vague and contradictory.

According to Rogers[3] an increase in carbon dioxide tension causes an increase in the depth of the respiratory movements in the goldfish, and the data collected by Bishop[4] indicate that it acts as a stimulant in the minnow and the perch. Black[5] has similar data for some other fish. Van Dam[6] had contradictory results with the eel. Two animals were tested; in the first 5–6 per cent of CO_2 brought on a great increase in the ventilation, but in the second several trials with different concentrations of CO_2 produced no dyspnoea and the breathing movements always slowed down, or even stopped altogether. Experiments with trout showed that a slight rise in the CO_2 tension resulted in a slight increase in the ventilation but water containing more than 2 per cent seemed to be very irritating and made the fish struggle violently. Fry[7] has a brief review of work on the subject and points out that the experimental evidence reported is on the whole fragmentary. He concludes that, except for the most sensitive species, the ordinary environmental levels of carbon dioxide have little influence on the rate of oxygen consumption. Here the emphasis is on the words 'ordinary environmental levels'; it will be shown that abnormally high tensions have a very marked effect.

One of the first to examine the effects of carbon dioxide on fish was Wells[8, 9] who carried out the work as part of a study on the toxicity of effluents from gas-works. Using a number of species for his tests Wells studied the effect of various combinations of oxygen and carbon dioxide, the oxygen concentration ranging from $0·1-0·15$ cm^3/l. to $8-10$ cm^3/l. and the carbon dioxide concentration from 1 cm^3/l. to $35-50$ cm^3/l. His results showed that provided that the oxygen supply is ample the fish tested can survive moderately high concentrations of CO_2. Thus in the 'high O_2 and high CO_2' tests, in which the oxygen concentration was $8-10$ cm^3/l. and the CO_2 concentration $35-50$ cm^3/l., the most sensitive of the species tested (*Moxostoma aureolum*, the red horse) survived about 34 h. As CO_2 has a density of about 2 mg/l. at s.t.p. $35-50$ cm^3/l. is about $70-100$ p.p.m. Other investigators have reported high values for the carbon dioxide threshold. King[10] states that brown trout, rainbow trout and brook trout showed no reaction at all to concentrations up to 200 p.p.m. At $300-500$ p.p.m. the gas appeared to act as an anaesthetic. The fish became stupefied and turned on their sides, but they lived for considerable periods with regular breathing movements. Doudoroff and Katz[1] consider that the values given by King are very high and that it is possible that all the concentrations reported by this author may be really p.p.m. of $CaCO_3$.

Fish[11] has shown that carbon dioxide is an effective anaesthetic for fingerling and adult salmon, which can be useful when the fish have to be handled and transported. Concentrations of 150–650 p.p.m. were tested and it was found that while the higher concentrations produced anaesthesia more rapidly, the period of exposure tolerated became shorter, and the fish might stop breathing and die. Adult steelhead trout and chinook salmon could remain in 400 p.p.m. CO_2 for 20 min after becoming insensible, with no apparent damage, though they showed some distress on being returned to normal water. The most suitable concentration proved to be 200 p.p.m. at which the fish gradually lost consciousness, turned over and sank to the bottom. Here they lay breathing at the usual rate but the amplitude of the opercular movements gradually grew less. If they ceased breathing the fish did not revive on being placed in normal water.

Carbon dioxide has a very important effect on fish respiration in that the concentration in which it is present determines the extent to which the available oxygen can be utilized. Black, Fry and Black[12] have made a comparative study of this effect with 16 species of fresh-water fish. The fish were sealed individually in bottles containing water in which the carbon dioxide tension varied from zero up to 200 mm Hg or more, while the oxygen content, in every case, was near air-saturation. When the fish died the ambient respired water was analysed, and it was found that as the carbon dioxide concentration was increased the residual oxygen increased, showing that less had been used. Thus, for example, when the initial carbon dioxide was zero the speckled trout would bring the oxygen tension down from 160 mm Hg to about 20 mm, but with carbon dioxide present at an initial tension of 120 mm the fish died with the oxygen tension at about 130 mm Hg. The same general result was seen with all the species tested but their resistance varied considerably (*Figure 43*). For every species there is a CO_2 tension which seems to inhibit oxygen utilization completely so that the fish begins to be asphyxiated at once. This is over 320 mm Hg for the brown bullhead but is only 80 mm Hg for the blacknose shiner. At 20° C a carbon dioxide tension of 80 mm Hg is equivalent to about 180 p.p.m.

Hynes[13] states that carbon dioxide may be produced in large amounts by the breakdown of organic matter and that up to 50 p.p.m. may occur in polluted water. Using running water supplies instead of the 'closed chamber' technique Alabaster, Herbert and Hemens[14] have shown that the oxygen thresholds for the rainbow trout are very dependent on the carbon dioxide tension. At 16·5° C with the CO_2 tension zero the fish survive over 24 h with the oxygen at 15 per cent saturation; at 30 p.p.m. CO_2 the water must be 25 per cent saturated to permit the same survival time; at 60 p.p.m. CO_2, 30–40 per cent. At 120 p.p.m. CO_2 the fish die in about 8 h in water saturated with oxygen and at 240 p.p.m. they live just over an hour. The oxygen consumption of the fish was not measured, but it would appear that as the fish lived over an hour at 240 p.p.m. even this concentration of CO_2 does not inhibit respiration completely. It is evident that any figures given for the tolerance of fish to carbon dioxide have little meaning unless the oxygen concentration is also specified. Some species are much more tolerant than others; tench are said to survive in water containing 20–43 p.p.m. of CO_2 when the oxygen concentration is only 1·7 p.p.m.[15]

Carbon monoxide is another constituent of gas-works effluents. Its effects on fish were studied by Wells[8, 9], who found that 1·2 cm³/l.

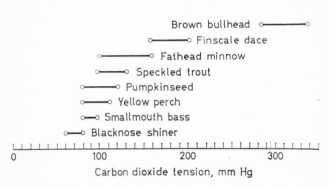

Figure 43. The effect of carbon dioxide on the respiration of various fish in 'closed chamber' experiments. For each fish the left-hand point gives the carbon dioxide tension at which the fish can utilize approximately half the available oxygen; the right-hand point gives the tension at which the fish can utilize none, so that it begins to be asphyxiated at once

(Drawn from the data of Black, Fry and Black[12].)

(about 1·5 p.p.m.) was fatal to sunfish and minnows (*Pimephales* and *Notropis*) but black bullheads survived 11·7 cm³/l. for nearly 10 h. Wells had found that water containing lethal amounts of carbon dioxide would soon become harmless on exposure to the air, and he expected the same thing to happen with carbon monoxide. Experiment, however, showed that solutions of this gas lost their toxic properties very slowly and might be fatal to fish after many days of exposure to the air. The extreme toxicity of carbon monoxide to man is well known and depends on its power of combining with haemoglobin. Its affinity for haemoglobin is said to be some 250 times that of oxygen, and as the carboxyhaemoglobin formed is useless for the transport of oxygen a tissue anoxia results.

One of the most important inorganic gases present in gas wastes and many chemical effluents is ammonia, and the toxicity of ammonia and ammonium salts to fish is a problem of some complexity which has attracted a great deal of attention. In solution in water ammonia acts as a weak base, and it forms salts with the acids, salts which hydrolyse to a considerable extent. Shelford[16] tested the effect of ammonia and its salts on the sunfish, *Lepomis humilis*, and found that the salts were far less toxic than the gas; thus a 7–8 p.p.m. solution of the gas killed in about 1 h, a solution of NH_4Cl of similar toxicity contained 700–800 p.p.m. Ellis[17] reviewed the literature published prior to 1937 and showed that there was evidence indicating that the toxicity of ammonium compounds was very dependent on the pH of the solution. His own experiments with the goldfish were carried out with ammonium carbonate, which was fatal at 100 p.p.m. and pH 7·7. Ellis estimated the lethal limit for ammonia to be about 2·5 p.p.m. for pH values between 7·4 and 8·5. Grindley[18] tested the effect of solutions of ammonium chloride on rainbow trout using distilled water, a hard water (Ca 278 p.p.m. as $CaCO_3$), and mixtures of the distilled and hard water in different proportions. The hard water solutions were the most toxic, the distilled water solutions the least toxic, and the mixtures were intermediate.

The explanation of the pH effect was provided by Wuhrmann, Zehender and Woker[19] and Wuhrmann and Woker[20], who showed that the toxicity of solutions of ammonia and ammonium salts depends on the concentration of molecular NH_3 or NH_4OH, the ammonium ion NH_4^+ being comparatively non-toxic. Neutrality or acidity tends towards the formation of ammonium ions; raising the pH increases the concentration of molecular ammonia. Since the pH of the solution is such an important factor the toxicity of ammonia is influenced by the carbon dioxide concentration, for the solution of this gas is weakly acid[21]. *Figure 44* shows how an increase in the concentration of carbon dioxide reduces the toxicity of a solution of ammonium chloride, but only up to a certain point, beyond which the carbon dioxide becomes lethal. The initial carbon dioxide concentration of the solution is not the only factor to be taken into account; the amount produced by the fish plays a part in determining the pH of the water at the gill surface. This is shown in a study by Lloyd and Herbert[22]. Lloyd[23] has published data for computing threshold concentrations for ammonia for rainbow trout which take into account the temperature, bicarbonate alkalinity, pH, dissolved oxygen, and concentration of free carbon dioxide. With all these variables the ammonia threshold can cover a very wide range. Thus, for example, for a bicarbonate alkalinity of 200 (p.p.m. as $CaCO_3$), the ammonia threshold in p.p.m. as N can be about 12 p.p.m. at a pH of 8·6 and more than 100 p.p.m. at pH 7·0. These threshold values can be up to 2½ times higher at low temperatures; much lower in water deficient in oxygen.

The relation between the toxicity of ammonia solutions and the concentration of undissociated ammonia or ammonium hydroxide suggests that ammonia acts on fish as a true internal poison entering the body by way of the gills, but the exact nature of its action is not understood. In man the inhalation of considerable quantities of the gas can produce a spasm of the glottis, and such swelling and congestion of the mucous membranes of the larynx and trachea that death

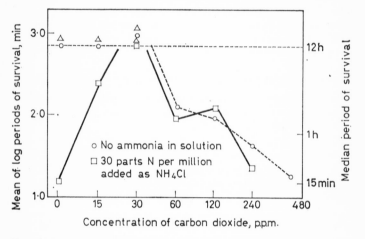

Figure 44. The toxicity of ammonia and carbon dioxide to rainbow trout at 17·5° C., with a dissolved oxygen concentration of 4·41 p.p.m.
(From *Water Pollution Research, 1954*[21], by courtesy of the *Journal of Experimental Biology*.)

may occur very suddenly from asphyxia[24]. It is possible that fish are affected in a similar way by high concentrations of ammonia; sticklebacks die suddenly with widely opened mouths[25].

Shelford[16] studied the reactions of fish to ammonia with the gradient tank, and found that they usually failed to recognize the solution and swam into it. The writer[25] has made some experiments with sticklebacks using an apparatus of the type shown in *Figure 8*, and four records are given in *Figure 45*. A very definite avoiding action was displayed towards the 0·04 N solution. At 0·01 N, though this concentration is highly toxic, the fish took some time to avoid it, and two of them died. With the 0·001 and 0·0001 N solutions a very definite 'positive' reaction was evident. The pH of the 0·04 N solution was 10·6;

sticklebacks do not avoid water of this pH if the alkalinity is due to sodium hydroxide.

Sulphur dioxide is another of the toxic inorganic gases found in gas wastes and various chemical effluents. In solution it forms the weak acid, sulphurous acid, which is readily oxidized to sulphuric acid. Sulphur dioxide is therefore a powerful reducing agent and it is this property that gives it a poisonous action upon protoplasm in general. In man the gas acts as an irritant poison and the few experiments carried out on fish with sulphurous acid showed that they are irritated at first and then intoxicated [16]. Chlorine is also an irritant poison, attacking the mucous membranes and producing severe pulmonary

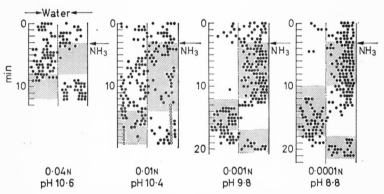

Figure 45. The reactions of sticklebacks to 0·04, 0·01, 0·001 and 0·0001 N ammonia. Survival times at these concentrations (in survival time experiments) 2 min, 4½ min, 35 min, 24 h plus. Temperature 16° C. Open circles represent dead fish

(By courtesy of the *Journal of Experimental Biology*.)

congestion and oedema in man. It is present in effluents from laundries and paper mills, in wastes from works carrying out the bleaching of textiles, and much is used, in the form of sodium hypochlorite, for the disinfection of water supplies and swimming baths. Its very high toxicity to fish has been known for a considerable time. Doudoroff and Katz [1] have reviewed the older literature and have shown that the results of a number of investigations indicate thresholds well below 1 p.p.m. Tests carried out at the Water Pollution Research Laboratory indicate that chlorine is very toxic to rainbow trout; with the oxygen concentration at 90 per cent saturation and the pH 6·3–8·2 the threshold is under 0·2 p.p.m.[26]. Eels and tench are said to be more resistant and the threshold for roach is about 0·4 p.p.m.[27].

Fish liberate a certain amount of ammonia into the water and ammonia may be present in various effluents discharged. Residual chlorine will combine with ammonia to form chloramines (NH_2Cl and $NHCl_2$) and nitrogen trichloride, NCl_3. Coventry, Shelford and Miller[28] found that chloramine concentrations of 0·76–1·2 p.p.m. were fatal to carp and bullheads; 0·4 p.p.m. killed trout and sunfish; and trout fry proved very sensitive, being killed in 48 h by 0·05–0·06 p.p.m. Merkens[29] has shown that when chlorine is added to water containing 0·1 p.p.m. of ammonia (p.p.m. as N), an amount commonly present in British rivers, various reactions occur, according to the quantity of chlorine added. A very small quantity is mostly converted to monochloramine (NH_2Cl), but when the Cl:N molar ratio is greater than one, dichloramine and nitrogen trichloride are formed, and complex reactions may occur in which some chlorine is lost by conversion to chloride ions. When the Cl:N ratio is still further increased most of the chloramines are destroyed and the chlorine added will be present as free chlorine. Despite these complexities the toxicity is clearly related to the total amount of residual chlorine present, which suggests that the toxicity of the chloramines and that of free chlorine must be of the same order. Merkens considers that for pollution control purposes it is best to assume that all residual chlorine present is in the form of free chlorine. He points out that since 0·08 p.p.m. of chlorine is fatal to trout in 7 days, the safe threshold must be very low, perhaps as low as 0·004 p.p.m. This estimate is based on extrapolation of the survival curve.

Allen, Blezard and Wheatland[30] have shown that certain effluents become very toxic when treated with chlorine, even when the doses are much smaller than those necessary to give residual chlorine. It appears that this results from the presence of thiocyanates in the effluent, derived from added gas-liquor. Thiocyanates react with chlorine to form cyanogen chloride $CNCl$:

$$KCNS + 4Cl_2 + 4H_2O = CNCl + KCl + H_2SO_4 + 6HCl$$

The reaction may be affected by the presence of substances, such as sulphide, which will react with the chlorine and reduce the amount available for the formation of cyanogen chloride. Survival and fatality curves for rainbow trout were worked out over the concentration range 0·1–0·45 p.p.m. $CNCl$, and indicated that the threshold of toxicity is below 0·1 p.p.m. It was found that the toxicity of these solutions could be reduced by aeration; to zero if the aeration was sufficiently prolonged. Aeration greatly reduced, but could not entirely remove, the toxicity of chlorinated sewage effluents containing gas liquor. Persistence of toxicity was most marked in effluents of high chlorine demand. It was concluded that the observations seemed to show that in these effluents some toxic substance was

THE INORGANIC GASES

formed which, unlike cyanogen chloride, was non-volatile. This compound differed from cyanogen chloride in another respect. Fish exposed to its action until they lost their balance did not recover on transference to fresh water. Fish removed from CNCl solutions on overturning usually revived, as they do after removal from a cyanide solution. According to Reed[31] cyanogen chloride has a toxic action essentially similar to that of hydrocyanic acid.

Some other inorganic gases have been reported to be toxic to fish, including phosphine, methane and ozone. Ozone has found use as a sterilizing agent for drinking-water, and has been proposed as an agent for the oxidation of cyanide wastes[32]. It appears to be highly toxic to fish. Hubbs[33] found that fish may be killed in less than an hour by water containing 0·03 p.p.m. of 'nascent oxygen'. The symptoms included irritation, irregular respiration, loss of equilibrium, wild rolling and dashing, and tetanus.

REFERENCES

[1] Doudoroff, P. and Katz, M. Critical review of the literature on the toxicity of industrial wastes to fish. I. Alkalis, acids and inorganic gases. *Sewage industr. Wastes*, 22 (1950) 1432–58
[2] Wright, S. *Applied Physiology*, 9th edn. 1952. London, New York and Toronto; Oxford Univ. Press
[3] Rogers, C. G. *Textbook of Comparative Physiology*. 1927. New York and London; McGraw-Hill
[4] Bishop, D. W. Respiration and metabolism. In *Comparative Animal Physiology*, ed. by C. L. Prosser. 1950. Philadelphia and London; Saunders
[5] Black, E. C. Respiration in fishes. In *Some Aspects of the Physiology of Fish. Univ. Toronto Stud. biol.*, 59 (1951) 91–111
[6] Van Dam, L. *On the Utilization of Oxygen and Regulation of Breathing in Some Aquatic Animals*. 1938. Groningen; Drukkerij 'Volharding'
[7] Fry, F. E. J. The aquatic respiration of fish. In *The Physiology of Fishes, Volume 1—Metabolism*, ed. by Margaret E. Brown. 1957. New York; Academic Press
[8] Wells, M. M. The resistance of fishes to different concentrations of carbon dioxide and oxygen. *Biol. Bull., Wood's Hole*, 25 (1913) 323–47
[9] Wells, M. M. The reactions and resistance of fishes to carbon dioxide and carbon monoxide. *Bull. Ill. Lab. nat. Hist.*, 11 (1918) 557–71
[10] King, J. E. Survival time of trout in relation to occurrence. *Amer. Midland Naturalist*, 29 (1943) 624–42
[11] Fish, F. F. The anaesthesia of fish by high carbon dioxide concentrations. *Trans. Amer. Fish. Soc.*, 72 (1942) 25–9
[12] Black, E. C., Fry, F. E. J. and Black, V. S. The influence of carbon dioxide on the utilization of oxygen by some fresh-water fish. *Canad. J. Zool.*, 32 (1954) 408–20
[13] Hynes, H. B. N. *The Biology of Polluted Waters*. 1960. Liverpool; Liverpool Univ. Press.

[14] Alabaster, J. S., Herbert, D. W. M. and Hemens, J.   The survival of rainbow trout (*Salmo gairdnerii* Richardson) and perch (*Perca fluviatilis* L.) at various concentrations of dissolved oxygen and carbon dioxide. *Ann. appl. Biol.*, 45 (1957) 177–88

[15] Weatherley, A. H.   Some features of the biology of the tench *Tinca tinca* (Linnaeus) in Tasmania. *J. anim. Ecol.*, 28 (1959) 73–87

[16] Shelford, V. E.   An experimental study of the effects of gas waste upon fishes, with especial reference to stream pollution. *Bull. Ill. Lab. nat. Hist.*, 11 (1917) 381–412

[17] Ellis, M. M.   Detection and measurement of stream pollution. *Bull. U.S. Bur. Fish.*, 48 (1937) 365–437

[18] Grindley, J.   Toxicity to rainbow trout and minnows of some substances known to be present in waste water discharged to rivers. *Ann. appl. Biol.*, 33 (1946) 103–12

[19] Wuhrmann, K., Zehender, F. and Woker, H.   Über die fischerei-biologische Bedeutung des Ammonium- und Ammoniakgehaltes fliessender Gewässern. *Vjschr. naturf. Ges. Zurich*, 92 (1947), 198–204

[20] Wuhrmann, K. and Woker, H.   Experimentelle Untersuchungen über die Ammoniak- und Blausäurevergiftung. *Schweiz. Z. Hydrol.*, 11 (1948) 210–44

[21] *Water Pollution Research, 1954.*   1955.   London; H.M.S.O.

[22] Lloyd, R. and Herbert, D. W. M.   The influence of carbon dioxide on the toxicity of un-ionized ammonia to rainbow trout (*Salmo gairdnerii* Richardson). *Ann. appl. Biol.*, 48 (1960) 399–404

[23] Lloyd, R.   The toxicity of ammonia to rainbow trout (*Salmo gairdnerii* Richardson). *Water & Waste Treatm. J.*, 8 (1961) 278–9

[24] Edmunds, C. W. and Gunn, J. A.   11th edn of *Cushny's Text-book of Pharmacology and Therapeutics.* 1936.   London; Churchill.

[25] Jones, J. R. E.   A further study of the reactions of fish to toxic solutions. *J. exp. Biol.*, 25 (1948) 22–34

[26] *Water Pollution Research, 1957.*   1958.   London; H.M.S.O.

[27] Desavelle, H. and Hubault, E.   Pollution of surface waters by trade waste waters. *Bull. du C.B.E.D.E.*, No. 14 (1951) 197–207.   Cited from *Summ. curr. Lit. Wat. Pollut.*, 26 (1953) 111

[28] Coventry, F. L., Shelford, V. E. and Miller, L. F.   The conditioning of a chloramine treated water supply for biological purposes. *Ecology*, 16 (1935) 60–66

[29] Merkens, J. C.   Studies on the toxicity of chlorine and chloramines to the rainbow trout. *Water & Waste Treatm. J.*, 7 (1958) 150–51

[30] Allen, L. A., Blezard, N. and Wheatland, A. B.   Formation of cyanogen chloride during chlorination of certain liquids; toxicity of such liquids to fish. *J. Hyg. Camb.*, 46 (1948) 184–93

[31] Reed, C. I.   The mechanism of the toxic action of cyanogen chloride. *J. Pharmacol.*, 15 (1920) 301–4

[32] Tyler, R. G., Maske, W., Westin, M. J. and Matthews, W.   Ozonation of cyanide wastes. *Sewage industr. Wastes*, 23 (1951) 1150–53

[33] Hubbs, C. L.   The high toxicity of nascent oxygen. *Phys. Zool.*, 3 (1930) 441–60

9

ACIDS AND ALKALIS: pH TOLERANCE LIMITS

MANY polluting effluents are highly acid; included in this type of waste are mine-water, iron pickle liquor, copper pickle liquor, wastes from DDT, viscose rayon, munition and battery factories, vinegar works and tanneries. Sulphuric acid is, perhaps, the most common acid present, but nitric, hydrochloric and phosphoric acids also occur and a considerable variety of other acids has been found in effluents from chemical works. Acids can affect fish in three different ways: first, by changing the pH of the stream into which they are discharged, without being directly lethal to fish, they can bring about changes in their conditions of existence and rate of growth which are not completely understood; secondly, they may be present in such concentrations as to be directly lethal, and thirdly, they may be harmful because they have anions of high toxicity or marked toxic properties as undissociated molecules. An example of this type is hydrocyanic acid, considered in Chapter 7.

Welch's statement[1] that innumerable papers have been published dealing with the hydrogen ion concentration of natural waters is no exaggeration, but the rôle of the hydrogen ion concentration in freshwater ecology is still something of a mystery. Some ecologists have maintained that the pH of natural waters is a supreme controlling factor determining the presence and distribution of aquatic organisms, but it is now generally recognized that this is not so. Nevertheless it is fairly clear that each aquatic organism has its toleration range of pH, terminated by a maximum and a minimum and with an optimum at some intermediate position. Fish are no exception to this rule and the pH range of some marine species is exceedingly narrow[2]. In a paper published in 1907, dealing with the Potomac, Marsh[3] expressed the view that to support fish life water must be alkaline; that when water became even slightly acid fish could not live in it. This, of course, is quite untrue. Many species can live in acid water, but it appears that under these conditions the fish may grow more slowly, and fail to attain the same size as other individuals of the same species living in alkaline streams. This was at one time attributed to differences in food supply. Menzies[4] has pointed out that there are qualitative differences between the invertebrate faunas of acid and alkaline streams; acid streams, though they may contain an abundance of animal life, are usually more or less devoid of crustacea and mollusca. Animals of these types are found, however, in certain lakes where the water is nearly neutral, such as Loch Leven, but here again, Menzies observes, there seems to be some factor restricting trout growth so that the presence or absence of crustacea and mollusca cannot be the whole explanation.

The classic study of this problem is that of Frost[5], dealing with the trout of the River Liffey in Ireland. The upper reaches of the Liffey have acid water ranging in pH from 4·6 to 6·8, normally about 5·6. The acidity is probably due to drainage from peat bogs. In the lower part of its course the river flows through an area of carboniferous limestone and its water becomes alkaline, the pH now ranging from 7·4 to 8·4, normally 7·8 to 8·0. The difference in pH between the upper and lower courses of the river appears to have a profound effect on the brown trout. In the acid upper reaches they grow slowly and are only about 20 cm in length when 5 years old; in the alkaline water of the lower reaches they grow more rapidly, attaining this size when only about 2 years old, and in 5 years they may be more than 32 cm long.

Frost carried out a long investigation into the reasons for this. The stomach contents of 349 fish from the upper part of the river and 228 from its lower course were examined and it appeared that the differences in rate of growth and size could not be explained on a basis of different diet and amount of food eaten. A further study by Frost[6] of the invertebrate fauna of the Liffey, showed that while differences existed between the invertebrate faunas of the upper and lower reaches, these differences in the available food supply did not appear to account for the marked differences in the size and growth rate of the fish in the two regions. In an experimental approach to the same problem Brown[7] found no differences in the early growth rates of trout fry reared for 5 months in Cambridge tap-water (hard) and fry grown in the same water 'softened'; with the calcium and bicarbonate ions reduced to about 5 p.p.m.; acidified with hydrochloric or nitric acid, or diluted with distilled water so that the salt content was cut to one-sixth. Brown points out that while there is considerable circumstantial evidence that *Salmo trutta* grows more rapidly in hard, alkaline waters than in soft, acid waters, no one has demonstrated unequivocally that fish growth rates are directly affected by the ionic composition of the water. Nevertheless the possibility must be taken into consideration when the pH of a stream is changed by acid effluents.

Pollution by acids may be sufficient to make the water of a stream not only less favourable for the growth of fish but directly lethal. A typical case is that noted by Lewis and Peters[8] who report on a study of the toxicity of strip coal mine slag drainage containing large quantities of acid-forming sulphur compounds. The effluent, from a mine in Illinois, had a pH of 2·3 and was toxic to fish when diluted up to 50 times, to a pH of about 4·0. In the case of hydrochloric, nitric and sulphuric acid, in which the degree of dissociation is high and little of the acid is present as un-ionized molecules, and in which the anions (Cl, NO_3, SO_4) are comparatively innocuous, the essential factor is the hydrogen ion concentration. There have been many studies of the toxicity of acids to fish; the literature published before 1950 has been reviewed by Doudoroff and Katz[9]. Of the earlier studies that of Ellis[10] is, perhaps, the most important. Ellis pointed out that experiments with low concentrations of mineral acids, in which the concentration is measured in p.p.m., are of little or no value, as the buffer substances and dissolved salts of the water used for making up the solutions will determine the amount of free hydrogen ions present. He carried out a large number of tests of the toxicity of acids to goldfish, and his tables give the concentrations in p.p.m. and the pH values of the solutions. Doudoroff and Katz have noted a number of curious discrepancies in the data; for example, the pH value of a solution containing 143 p.p.m. of sulphuric acid (0·0029 N) is given as 3·5, while a solution containing 200 p.p.m. of nitric acid (0·0032 N) had a pH of 4·9.

For a survival time of at least 4 days the limiting pH values were: sulphuric acid, 4·0; hydrochloric and citric acids, 4·5; lactic acid, 4·6; nitric and tartaric acids, 4·9; acetic acid, 5·5; oxalic acid, 5·8; benzoic acid, 5·9; chromic acid, 7·3, and tannic acid, 7·8. These values are for solutions made up with a hard water of pH 7·8–8·0. The very great differences in these limiting pH values indicate at once that in some cases the hydrogen ions are not the only toxic agent present; chromic acid and tannic acid are toxic even in alkaline solutions. The undissociated molecules of the weaker acids, or their anions, evidently contribute to the toxic effect to a greater or less extent.

Ellis concluded that 'fishes are killed by acid wastes first through the precipitation and coagulation of the mucus on the gills and by the coagulation of the gill membranes themselves. If this coagulation of the gills and gill secretions does not take place, the death of the fish is attributable to the lethal action of the kation of the acid.' Evidently here, and throughout his discussion, Ellis meant to say 'anion' instead of 'kation'. He goes on to explain that a combination of the two effects may occur; precipitation of mucus and damage to the gill filaments by the hydrogen ions may be supplemented by a specific toxic action. Reviewing all his data Ellis concludes that the truly acid effects must be limited to acids which kill at hydrogen ion concentrations more acid than pH 5·0, and that in the case of acids which kill at hydrogen ion concentrations less acid than pH 5·0, lethal factors other than hydrogen ion concentration play a major part. Water more acid than pH 5·0 may be tolerated for a considerable period but may be detrimental eventually; in these cases, however, a distinction must be made between water rendered acid by the presence of carbon dioxide or peaty matter, and water containing mineral acids.

Carpenter[11] studied the tolerance of minnows (*Phoxinus phoxinus*) to nitric acid solutions. At pH values of 4·4, 4·6 and 4·8 the survival time was 7–7½ h. At 5·0 the survival time lengthened to 27½–28 h and solutions of pH 5·2 appeared to have no effect in 3 days. Assuming a complete dissociation, nitric acid of pH 4·4 would be about 0·00004 N. Sodium nitrate solutions much more concentrated than this have little or no toxicity to fish, so the lethal action of nitric acid at pH 4·4 is evidently attributable to the hydrogen ions. Sticklebacks seem to have the same pH limit; tested with hydrochloric acid solutions they die in about 77 h at pH 4·4, in about 5½ days at 4·8, and live about the same time as controls at 5·0[12].

Westfall[13], in his study of coagulation film anoxia in fish, determined the tolerance of goldfish to solutions of sulphuric acid, and showed that the toxicity of the solutions was greatly increased when the available oxygen supply was reduced. Stiemke and Eckenfelder[14] have also tested the resistance of fish to mineral acids. The fish used in this case were bluegills, and the tolerance limits determined for hydrochloric, nitric, sulphuric and phosphoric acid were on the acid side of pH 4·0. On the basis of their results Stiemke and Eckenfelder formulated a relationship which, they claimed, made it possible to predict the effect of any concentration or resulting pH of an acid industrial waste on the survival of fish. Doudoroff and Katz[9] have pointed out that the outstanding feature of their formula is its derivation from a series of tests in which distilled water was the only diluent; that there is no evidence that its applicability to natural stream waters had been considered, and that inasmuch as there are abundant reasons for questioning such applicability the formula appears to have almost no validity from a practical standpoint. The main weakness of the experimental work of Stiemke and Eckenfelder is the shortness of the exposure periods; in some cases the test period was only 30 min, in others it was 4 h and in a few experiments, 24 h. Their figures for the tolerance of bluegills to hydrochloric acid resemble those obtained by the writer for sticklebacks[12], and in many instances their data are in close agreement with Ellis's data for goldfish; thus sulphuric acid was fatal to the bluegills in 4 h at pH 3·8; at pH 3·9 the same acid is fatal to the goldfish in 5–6 h.

Doudoroff and Katz have also reviewed and criticized a number of other papers dealing with the resistance of fish to acids. The general conclusions reached are, that where the hydrogen ion concentration is the only factor concerned, the tolerance limit for most fish is about pH 5·0, though water of a somewhat higher degree of acidity may be endured for a limited period by the more resistant species; that waters with a pH above 5·0 can be tolerated indefinitely by most freshwater fish in the absence of other adverse factors; that for successful reproduction, at least in the case of more sensitive species, there are some doubts about the suitability of waters with a pH near 5·0. The speckled trout is a species of very wide pH range; 4·1–9·5 according to Creaser[15]. The pike, the yellow perch and the bullhead are also very tolerant types; Brown and Jewell[16] found that they would survive abrupt transfer from water of pH 4·4–6·4 to water of pH 8·2–8·7.

In experimental work on the tolerance of fish to acidity, hydrochloric acid is probably the best acid to use for making up the solutions, as it is highly dissociated and the chloride ion is one of the least toxic of the anions. Bishai has pointed out that early investigators used various acids for the preparation of water of high acidity[17]; hydrochloric acid, sulphuric acid, acetic acid and carbon dioxide have all been employed. Bishai has studied the pH tolerance of young and larval fish. Using carbon dioxide for the preparation of acid water he found the tolerance level for young alevins of the salmon, the sea trout and the brown trout to be 6·0–6·2. This seems a very mild degree of acidity and the lethal effect of the water of lower pH may have been due to the presence of an excess of carbon dioxide, not to pure acidity. Nevertheless, high acidity in natural waters is often associated with the presence of an excess of carbon dioxide and Bishai recognized that 'the effect of low pH caused by the presence of carbon dioxide in water may be more pronounced than the same pH caused by mineral acids'. Krishna[18], using water the pH of which was altered by the addition of hydrochloric acid or sodium hydroxide, found that day-old larvae of the trout would survive water of a pH between 4·0 and 5·0; unfortunately he does not state the exposure time.

It is not clear as to how fish adjust themselves to varying conditions of pH within their normal range of tolerance. Jobes and Jewell[19] carried out an investigation to find whether a relation exists between the alkali reserve of the blood of fish and the pH of their environment. They made determinations of the alkali reserve of bullheads taken from an acid lake (pH 6·2–7·2) and an alkaline lake (pH 8·4–8·6), and found no correlation between the alkali reserve and the pH of the water. Fish varying widely in alkali reserve were taken at the same time and place, and fish having the same reserve could be taken from waters very different chemically.

The effect on fish of acids in which the anions or the undissociated molecules are toxic may now be examined further. Provided that the cation is of low toxicity a salt of an acid of this type will have an effect similar to that of the parent acid, since on ionization it will yield the same anion, or it may form the acid by hydrolysis. No really comprehensive comparative study of the toxicity of acids to fish has been carried out, nor has any investigator tested a complete range of sodium salts, to place the anions in order of toxicity. Some studies on these lines have been made with invertebrates, such as that by the writer[20], dealing with the planarian *Polycelis nigra*, and that by Anderson[21] with the water-flea *Daphnia magna*.

In the case of some acids, for example hydrocyanic acid discussed in Chapter 7, the nature of their toxic effect is well understood; in the case of others little useful information appears to be available. Ellis[10] believed that tannic acid formed insoluble compounds with certain protein constituents of the gill tissues. Experimental and clinical studies of the value of tannic acid as a treatment for burns have shown that it is a hepatotoxic agent which can cause a severe central necrosis of the liver if absorbed in appreciable amounts[22]. Whether a similar effect is produced in fish is not known. Ellis believed that chromic acid was another of the substances whose effect is to destroy the efficiency of the respiratory organs, but Fromm and Schiffman[23] have shown that this is not so. In a study of the toxicity of potassium chromate to largemouth bass they observed no significant changes in the histology of the gills, but severe pathological changes were seen in the intestine immediately posterior to the pyloric caeca. There appeared to be a widespread destruction of the intestinal epithelium, which sloughed off almost entirely, so that the digestive function of the gut must have been seriously impaired, if not destroyed completely. Fromm and Schiffman consider it unlikely that chromium reaches the gut as a result of drinking, for freshwater fish drink little or no water. They think it is possible that chromium enters the fish via the gills, is excreted in part by the liver, and so reaches the gut in the bile. Hexavalent chromium, as chromic acid or chromates, is present in wastes associated with chromium plating, tanning and the anodizing of aluminium. The toxicity to fish appears to be rather low; Fromm and Schiffman found that the 48 h TL_m value for largemouth bass was 195 p.p.m.

Oxalic acid is generally believed to be poisonous because it precipitates calcium, removing from solution an element essential for life. No satisfactory measurements of its toxicity to fish appear to have been made; most of Ellis's experiments were made with hard water, so that most of the acid must have been precipitated. Westfall[13] believes that lactic acid is a true internal poison in fish; he discusses its effects on protoplasm and its power of producing rigour in muscles. The toxicity of acetic acid is largely due to its high penetrative powers; it enters living cells so quickly as to produce much swelling and in this way it can produce an acute congestion of a fish's respiratory organs. Fluorides have a marked effect on fish; the symptoms of acute fluoride intoxication in carp and rainbow trout include lethargy and anorexia, followed later by violent and erratic movement. Shortly before death the fish lose their equilibrium and there are tremors of the muscles. At 15° C the TL_m for the rainbow trout is 2·7–4·7 p.p.m. F (480 h experiment); carp are very much more resistant; at 18–24° C their TL_m is 75–91 p.p.m. F. In both cases the tolerance limit varies somewhat with the calcium content of the water[24].

Wastes associated with tanning, wool scouring, the mercerizing of cotton and the manufacture of certain chemicals may contain caustic soda, sodium carbonate or lime. Such alkaline effluents may have a pH of 12–14 and can be lethal to all types of stream life, including the bacteria[25]. Apart from the many studies made of the toxicity of ammonia the effect of alkalis on fish has not claimed the same amount of attention as the effect of acids. Doudoroff and Katz[9] are of the opinion that many papers dealing with the toxicity of the strong alkalis (sodium, potassium and calcium hydroxide) are of limited value, as the pH of the experimental solutions is not stated, and no measures were adopted to maintain their alkalinity at the initial value. In the course of prolonged tests the neutralizing effect of the carbon dioxide produced by the fish may be an important disturbing factor.

In cases of damage to fisheries by highly alkaline effluents the cation of the alkali concerned, usually sodium or potassium, is of minor importance, and the concentration of OH ions, as indicated by the pH, is the factor to be considered. Wiebe[26] has shown that some fish will tolerate a sudden rise of alkalinity; he found that goldfish, largemouth bass and green sunfish survived transfer from water with a pH near to 7·0 to water of pH 9·3–9·6. In the experiments of Sanborn[27] goldfish, largemouth bass and bluegills survived flowing water of pH 10·4–10·5 for 7 days, but all died in 2–5 h at pH 11·1. The rainbow trout seems to tolerate alkaline water up to a pH of about 9·8 and the limit seems to be about the same for acclimatization pH values of 6·55, 7·50 and 8·40. This is shown in *Figure 46* which also gives the results of similar experiments in the acid range[28].

A number of experiments have been made to test the reactions of fish to acids and alkalis. Wells[29], using the gradient tank apparatus described in Chapter 3, studied the reactions of bluegills, white crappies, green-spotted sunfish and bullheads. He concluded that these fish are negative to neutral water, in favour of slight acidity or slight alkalinity; that their normal choice was slight acidity, about 0·00005 N H_2SO_4. It is difficult to estimate the pH this concentration of acid would provide as the water used by Wells was alkaline, containing up to 70 p.p.m. of calcium. According to Shelford[30],

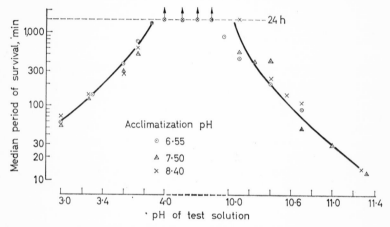

Figure 46. The effect of acclimatization pH values on the survival of rainbow trout in acid and alkaline solutions. Temperature 17.0° C ± 1·0°C

(From *Water Pollution Research 1961*[28], by permission of the Controller of H.M. Stationery Office.)

Wells took neutrality to be the 'turning point' of phenolphthalein, presumably about pH 9. Brown and Jewell[16] noted that three fish—pike, yellow perch and bullhead—were found in an acid lake and in an adjacent one with alkaline water. They carried out experiments with a tank in which water taken from the acid lake flowed in at one end and water from the alkaline lake flowed in at the opposite end. Placed in this tank the pike, yellow perch and bullheads selected the type of water to which they were accustomed, while some speckled trout collected from a body of water intermediate in pH value selected the middle zone.

The writer[31] has studied the reactions of *Gasterosteus aculeatus* to acid and alkaline water over the pH range 3·2–12·0, using the reaction tube apparatus described in Chapters 3 and 6. In every case the fish were offered acid or alkaline water as an alternative to a very soft tap-water of pH 6·8. The acid or alkaline water was supplied by a dripper arrangement in which hydrochloric acid or sodium hydroxide of suitable concentration was diluted about 100 times.

To water of pH 6·0–7·0 the fish appear indifferent. At 5·8 a somewhat indefinite negative reaction is displayed and water of a pH below this is avoided; the time taken for the reaction to develop dropping quite sharply down to pH 5·0 and, thereafter, more slowly

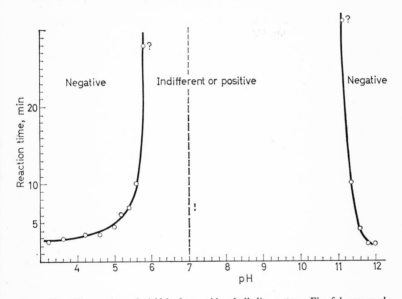

Figure 47. The reactions of sticklebacks to acid and alkaline water. Five fish were used for each reaction time determination. Temperature 14° C

(By courtesy of the *Journal of Experimental Biology*.)

(*Figure 47*). On the alkaline side, water of pH 7·0–11·0 seems to excite no response but at 11·4 a fairly definite negative reaction is developed. Still more alkaline water is rejected very quickly; on meeting it the fish gasps, with widely opened mouth and obvious signs of distress. The stickleback is thus far more tolerant of alkalinity, and the data reviewed by Doudoroff and Katz suggests that this may hold for many other fish. The explanation may be that the carbon dioxide given off at the gill surface may have some effect in reducing the pH in the immediate neighbourhood of the gill filaments, thus giving some degree of protection. There is evidence that fish bring about changes in the water surrounding them; in the experiments of

Brown[7] on the effect of pH changes on the growth rate of young trout, attempts to keep the water acid by adding small quantities of decinormal hydrochloric or nitric acid were not successful, because the acid was neutralized by the ammonia produced by the fish.

REFERENCES

[1] Welch, P. S. *Limnology*, 2nd edn. 1952. New York, Toronto and London; McGraw-Hill

[2] Atkins, W. A. R. The hydrogen ion concentration of sea water in its biological relations. *J. Mar. biol. Ass. U.K.*, n.s. 12 (1919–22) 717–71

[3] Marsh, M. C. The effect of some industrial wastes on fishes. In *The Potomac river basin, U.S. Geol. Surv., Water-supply and irrigation paper No. 192*, Washington 1907, pp. 337–48

[4] Menzies, W. J. M. *Sea Trout and Trout*. 1936. London; Arnold

[5] Frost, W. E. River Liffey survey—II. The food consumed by the brown trout (*Salmo trutta* Linn.) in acid and alkaline waters. *Proc. R. Irish Acad.*, 45 B (1939) 139–206

[6] Frost, W. E. River Liffey survey—IV. The fauna of the submerged 'mosses' in an acid and an alkaline water. *Proc. R. Irish Acad.*, 47 B (1942) 293–369

[7] Brown, M. E. Experimental studies on growth. In *The Physiology of Fishes, Volume 1—Metabolism*, ed. by Margaret E. Brown. 1957. New York; Academic Press

[8] Lewis, W. M. and Peters, C. Coal mine slag drainage. *Industr. Wastes*, 1 (1956) 145–7

[9] Doudoroff, P. and Katz, M. Critical review of literature on the toxicity of industrial wastes and their components to fish, I. Alkalis, acids and inorganic gases. *Sewage industr. Wastes*, 22 (1950) 1432–58

[10] Ellis, M. M. Detection and measurement of stream pollution. *Bull. U.S. Bur. Fish.*, 48 (1937) 365–437

[11] Carpenter, K. E. The lethal action of soluble metallic salts on fishes. *Brit. J. exp. Biol.*, 4 (1927) 378–90

[12] Jones, J. R. E. The relation between the electrolytic solution pressures of the metals and their toxicity to the stickleback (*Gasterosteus aculeatus* L.). *J. exp. Biol.*, 16 (1939) 425–37

[13] Westfall, B. A. Coagulation film anoxia in fishes. *Ecology*, 26 (1945) 283–7

[14] Stiemke, R. E. and Eckenfelder, W. W. A practical method for predicting the effects of common acids and alkalis on the survival of fish. *N.C. State College Rec.*, 46 (1947) 45 pp.

[15] Creaser, C. W. Relative importance of hydrogen-ion concentration, temperature, dissolved oxygen and carbon dioxide tension on habitat selection by brook trout. *Ecology*, 11 (1930) 246–62

[16] Brown, H. W. and Jewell, M. E. Further studies on the fishes of an acid lake. *Trans. Amer. micr. Soc.*, 45 (1926) 20–34

[17] Bishai, H. M. The effect of hydrogen ion concentration on the survival and distribution of larval and young fish. *Z. wissenschaftliche Zool.*, 164 (1960) 107–18

[18] Krishna, D. Effect of changing pH on developing trout eggs and larvae. *Nature*, 171 (1953) 434

[19] Jobes, F. W. and Jewell, M. E.   Studies on the alkali reserve of the blood of *Ameiurus nebulosus* from acid and basic waters.   *Trans. Amer. micr. Soc.*, 46 (1927) 175–86

[20] Jones, J. R. E.   A study of the relative toxicity of anions with *Polycelis nigra* as test animal.   *J. exp. Biol.*, 18 (1941) 170–81

[21] Anderson, B. G.   The toxicity thresholds of various sodium salts determined by the use of *Daphnia magna*.   *Sewage Wks J.*, 18 (1946) 82–7

[22] Goodman, L. S. and Gilman, A.   *The Pharmacological Basis of Therapeutics*, 2nd edn.   1955.   New York; Macmillan

[23] Fromm, P. O. and Schiffman, R. H.   Toxic action of hexavalent chromium on largemouth bass.   *J. Wildlife Mgmt*, 22 (1958) 40–44

[24] Neuhold, J. M. and Sigler, W. F.   Effects of sodium fluoride on carp and rainbow trout.   *Trans. Amer. Fish. Soc.*, 89 (1960) 358–70

[25] Klein, L.   *Aspects of River Pollution*.   1957.   London; Butterworths

[26] Wiebe, A. H.   Notes on the exposure of several species of pond fishes to sudden changes of pH.   *Trans. Amer. micr. Soc.*, 50 (1931) 380–93

[27] Sanborn, N. H.   The lethal effect of certain chemicals on fresh water fish.   *Canning Tr.*, 67 (1945) 10–12; 26

[28] *Water Pollution Research 1961*.   1962.   London; H.M.S.O.

[29] Wells, M. M.   Reactions and resistance of fishes in their natural environment to acidity, alkalinity and neutrality.   *Biol. Bull., Wood's Hole*, 29 (1915) 221–57

[30] Shelford, V. E.   *Laboratory and Field Ecology*.   1929.   London; Balliere

[31] Jones, J. R. E.   A further study of the reactions of fish to toxic solutions.   *J. exp. Biol.* 25 (1948) 22–34

10

SYNTHETIC DETERGENTS AND SOAPS

SYNTHETIC detergents were first used in the 1930's but it was after the war of 1939–45 that they became popular and began to displace the 'natural' detergents or soaps, made from sodium palmitate, sodium oleate and sodium stearate. In 1948 the synthetic detergents accounted for 16 per cent of the market for cleaning agents and in 1956 the proportion had risen to 70 per cent. They began to attract the attention of scientists interested in water pollution soon after the war; one of the first troubles to be noted was the presence of masses of foam on rivers, foam caused by the presence of residual detergent which had survived treatment at the sewage works. The River Lee at Luton was one of the first rivers to attract attention in this respect[1].

The possibility that synthetic detergents might be toxic to fish was soon investigated. Schmassmann[2] was one of the first to carry out experiments; he used three different preparations, one of unknown composition from Germany, and two fatty-acid condensation products prepared in Switzerland, one of which contained pyridine. In the solutions of the detergent containing pyridine the respiration of the fish appeared to be affected, and some of them exposed to dilute solutions (10–40 p.p.m.) for some hours and then transferred to water showed symptoms of a delayed toxic effect, characterized by paralysis and loss of equilibrium. Further tests seemed to show that the fatty acid was responsible for the effects on respiration, while the pyridine was the substance causing the nervous symptoms. The German detergent proved to be more toxic than the Swiss preparations; a 20 p.p.m. solution was fatal in about 12 h but fish exposed to 10 p.p.m. solutions until they developed some loss of equilibrium recovered on being placed in fresh water, without symptoms of a delayed toxic action. Schmassmann concluded that the strong wetting action of the detergents adversely affected gas exchange at the respiratory surfaces.

An undated publication by Oldham[3] issued about this time describes some tests made on carp with solutions of a non-ionic detergent, Lissapol N, a condensation product of ethylene oxide and an alkylated phenol. Concentrations of 20, 25 and 50 p.p.m. were tested, for long periods, with little harmful effect. The non-ionic detergents do not ionize at all in aqueous solution. Most detergents do ionize, giving a positively charged ion which is usually sodium, and a negatively charged ion of somewhat complex structure, including a long hydrocarbon chain. Examples of these anionic detergents are 'Dreft' and 'Teepol', which are sodium alkyl sulphates, and 'Tide' and 'Daz', which are alkyl aryl sulphonates.

The first experiments made to test the effect of detergents of this type on freshwater animals by Degens et al.[4] and by Leclerc and Devlaminck[5] gave results markedly different from those obtained with the non-ionic preparations used by Oldham. The sodium alkyl sulphate and alkyl aryl sulphonate tested by Degens et al. proved to be toxic to sticklebacks, roach and carp at a concentration of only 5 p.p.m. However, it was found that the fish could be acclimatized to much higher concentrations than this if the concentration was low to start with, and gradually raised. In some cases even 36 p.p.m. was tolerated after a gradual build-up. Leclerc and Devlaminck, using minnows as the test fish, investigated the effects of sodium lauryl sulphate and sodium dodecyl benzene sulphonate. Both these anionic detergents proved to be decidedly toxic, the limiting concentration being 6–7 p.p.m. of active ingredient. Tests with a hard water and distilled water gave very similar results. Another detergent they tested was a polyglycol ether, and this also proved to be decidedly toxic, the limiting concentration being 10–11 p.p.m. of the entire product, or 2–3 p.p.m. of active ingredient. Like Schmassmann, Leclerc and Devlaminck noted that the respiration of the fish appeared to be affected; at death the minnows had widely opened mouths and their gill covers were raised. Before death there was some trembling of the fins, but apart from this the fish displayed no symptoms of nervous disturbance.

In 1956 the Committee on Synthetic Detergents[6] reported concentrations of detergent in British rivers ranging from 0·2 to 4·9 p.p.m., the higher value being for a stream containing undiluted sewage, and a study of an effluent from a sewage works in Hertfordshire, carried on over a period of several months, showed a concentration of anionic surface-active material ranging from 3 to 6 p.p.m. The possibility that fish might be exposed, in British rivers, to concentrations of detergent of this order for long periods of time prompted an investigation at the Water Pollution Research Laboratory[7]. Exact information on the composition of the synthetic washing powders on the market was not available. Taking this into consideration and also the likelihood that the pollution would probably be due to a mixture of different types it was decided to carry out tests with rainbow trout using a mixture of equal weights of seven popular detergents ('Daz',

'Dreft', 'Fab', 'Spel', 'Surf', 'Tide' and 'Wisk'); it was hoped that this mixture would contain all the ingredients of detergents normally present, in approximately the proportions which occur in domestic sewage. In most of the experiments 10 fish were placed in 30–40 l. of solution; the solutions were kept well aerated, and renewed each day.

In the 10 solutions the concentration of the detergent mixture varied from 10 to 50 p.p.m. The concentration of surface-active material, as determined by analysis, varied from 2·12 to 12·4 p.p.m.

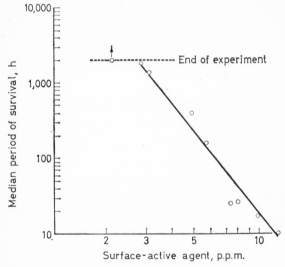

Figure 48. Survival times of rainbow trout in solutions of a mixture of synthetic detergents. Concentrations are p.p.m. surface-active material as determined by analysis. Temperature 17.5° C

(After Herbert *et al.*[7], by permission of the Controller of H.M. Stationery Office, Crown copyright reserved.)

so that the essential ingredient formed about 20–26 per cent of the mixture. Proprietary brands of synthetic detergent are not composed entirely of surface-active agent; various other chemicals are added to act as 'builders', these make up 74–80 per cent of the product as packed. The result of this series of experiments is given by *Figure 48*. Here the concentration of anionic surface-active material is plotted against the survival times. Both scales are logarithmic and it will be seen that the log/log relationship is linear. The survival time exceeds 10 days at 4 p.p.m., and approaches 100 days at 3 p.p.m.

The possible toxic effects of the ingredients added as builders, bleachers, etc., was next investigated. Solutions of each of the separate substances known to be included in typical washing powders were prepared, in concentrations equivalent to a solution of the whole product containing 10 p.p.m. of surface-active agent. The first series of experiments had shown that solutions containing this amount were fatal in rather less than 24 h. The actual concentrations of the various substances are given in column 2 of Table 7 and it will be seen that no fish died within 24 h (column 3). All would presumably have been killed by the surface-active agent if that were also present. The further columns in Table 7 give the results with tests of multiples of this basic concentration, and it will be seen that no fish died in concentrations up to 8 times the basic. These results seem to show that the subsidiary ingredients of synthetic washing powders have no toxic effect of importance. It is possible that they do augment the toxicity of the surface-active agent; this is suggested

Table 7. Toxicity of Typical 'Building' Ingredients in Synthetic Detergent Washing Powders to Rainbow Trout*

Substance	Lowest concentration tested p.p.m.	Per cent dead after 24 h in the following multiples of the lowest concentration tested						
		×1	×2	×4	×8	×16	×32	×64
Sodium sulphate	11·0	0	0	0	0	0	0	0
Sodium silicate	4·0	0	0	0	0	0	0	0
Sodium tripolyphosphate	17·5†	0	0	0	0	0	0	0
Sodium pyrophosphate	17·5†	0	0	0	0	0	0	100
Carboxymethyl cellulose	0·5	0	0	0	0	0	0	0
Sodium perborate	5·0	0	0	0	0	0	0	80
A fatty-acid alkylolamide	1·5	0	0	0	0	100	100	100

* The concentrations in column 2 are those equivalent to 10 p.p.m. surface-active material in a typical detergent formulation. From Herbert et al.[7].
† Each concentration equivalent to the total phosphate concentration in the typical formulation; the relative quantities of these two phosphates used is variable.

by the observation that solutions of pure sodium tetrapropylene benzene sulphonate are slightly less toxic than solutions of washing powders containing approximately the same quantity of this reagent. It is not possible to be certain about this as the surface-active agent in the washing powders may not have been chemically identical with the pure product used.

Further experiments were made to test the extent to which the toxicity of residual surface-active material in sewage treated by the activated-sludge process, or with percolating filters, is influenced by the various other materials in the effluent. The results would appear to indicate that the toxicity is lessened, to a considerable extent, but the reasons for this require further investigation. It is possible that a proportion of the surface-active material is adsorbed on suspended matter in the effluent. The oxygen content is important; if the concentration is below 5 p.p.m. there is a marked increase in the toxicity of a solution of surface-active material. Furthermore it has been shown that the oxygen balance of flowing water is affected by the presence of surface-active agents; the addition of only 1 p.p.m. will bring about a considerable reduction in the rate at which oxygen is absorbed[8]. In cases of pollution by detergents a consideration of the oxygen content of the affected stream is very necessary. The general conclusion drawn from the whole investigation was that in British rivers synthetic detergents seemed unlikely to be a serious danger to fish, provided that the amount of surface-active material present did not exceed 3 p.p.m., and provided that the oxygen supply was adequate.

The chief American study of the same problem is that of Henderson, Pickering and Cohen[9], who carried out an investigation of the effects of the various components of synthetic detergents (or 'syndets') on fathead minnows and bluegills. They noted that while no major damage to fisheries appeared to have been caused by these substances in the U.S.A., the consumption of detergents was rising, that the concentration of syndets in the sewage of various American cities was reported to range from 4 to 45 p.p.m., and that up to 6 p.p.m. and even more, might be present in some American rivers.

In the first series of tests with the minnows, 24, 48 and 96 h median tolerance limits were determined for five packaged household detergents ('Cheer', 'Tide', 'Dreft', 'Felso' and 'Vel') as sold retail. These were all tested separately, not as a mixture. Analyses showed that the different products were of fairly similar composition; all contained 18–30 per cent of surface-active material or 'surfactant' and various amounts of builders, mostly sodium tripolyphosphate. In each individual experiment five fish were placed in 10 l. of solution in a glass vessel. Two types of water were used: a naturally hard, limestone water obtained from springs, and a very soft water prepared in the laboratory by mixing 95 parts of distilled, demineralized water and five parts of natural spring water. The temperature was maintained at 25° C, and as the fish were small, up to 2 in. in length, no aeration of the solutions was necessary.

All five products were toxic to the minnows, the 96 h median tolerances ranging from 41 to 85 p.p.m. of the packed detergent in soft water. In hard water the toxicity, in some cases, was much higher, the 96 h tolerances for the various types ranging from 15–87 p.p.m. None of the preparations had any significant effect on the pH and oxygen content of the water. Further experiments were made to evaluate the toxicity of the different components of the detergents. A number of samples of anionic alkyl benzene sulphonates was obtained. Analyses showed these to have very different degrees of purity, one being 100 per cent alkyl benzene sulphonate, the others containing 85, 60 and 40 per cent; the inactive material was mostly sodium sulphate. Two further types of surfactant were also tested; these were sodium lauryl sulphate and the non-ionic type, polyoxyethylene ester.

The results with minnows are summarized in Table 8. Only one set of tests was made with bluegills, with alkyl benzene sulphonate Sample 1, and the soft water. The bluegills appeared to be a little more resistant than the minnows. It will be seen that for the alkyl benzene sulphonate samples of high concentration (Samples 1 and 2) the limiting concentrations of 3·5–4·5 p.p.m. are very similar to those determined for the rainbow trout at the Water Pollution Research Laboratory. The data cannot be compared very closely as the

Table 8. 96 h Median Tolerance Limits for Fathead Minnows in Various Surfactants and Builders *

	Degree of purity (per cent)	TL_m p.p.m. (soft water)	TL_m p.p.m. (hard water)
SURFACTANT			
Alkyl benzene sulphonate			
Sample 1 . . .	·100	4·5	3·5
Sample 2 . . .	85	4·2	4·4
Sample 3 . . .	60	15	8·5
Sample 4 . . .	40	23	12
Sodium lauryl sulphate .	100?	5·1	5·9
Polyoxyethylene ester .	100	37	38
BUILDER			
Sodium tripolyphosphate .		140	1,300
Sodium sulphate . .		9,000	13,500

* From the data in Henderson, Pickering and Cohen[9].

maximum exposure times are very different and the fathead minnow tests were run at a much higher temperature than that selected for the trout. The American work agrees with the British in showing that the builder ingredients have no important toxic potential. After a detailed review of their results and those of other workers, Henderson, Pickering and Cohen conclude that while some types of surfactant may be of comparatively low toxicity, the alkyl benzene sulphonates are highly toxic, in hard and soft water, that 3·5 p.p.m. can cause a 50 per cent mortality of moderately sensitive fish in a relatively short time, and that concentrations rather less than this may have a harmful effect over long periods. The information available about the surfactant content of British and American rivers suggests that some of these are running up to or over the danger level.

Further work on detergents has been carried out at the Deception Pass Marine Research Station of the Department of Fisheries, Washington[10]. Rainbow trout, chinook, chum and silver salmon have been used as the test fish in this investigation. The results with the different detergents tested are summarized separately:

(1) 'Blast.' This reagent apparently contained no intrinsically toxic substance. Moderately high concentrations were fatal to the fish mainly because of the high alkalinity of the solutions. The fish exhibited many symptoms of distress and at death were excessively slimy, with opaque corneas.

(2) 'Gamlen–CW.' This is a detergent used to precipitate paint from the surface of water. The fish tested showed many symptoms of irritation and intoxication, including spasmodic snapping of the jaws, violent activity, and twitching of the eyes and fins. Only chinook salmon were tested and the critical level appeared to lie between 10 and 17·8 p.p.m. in aerated sea-water.

(3) 'Santomerse–D.' Only one set of experiments was carried out with this detergent. Silver salmon fingerlings were tested with 1–20 p.p.m. solutions and a 10 p.p.m. solution gave a total kill in under 23 h.

(4) 'Sterox–SE.' This is stated to be a 100 per cent active, non-ionic type; a yellow liquid soluble in water in all proportions giving solutions having a pH of 6–8. It did not appear to be of very high toxicity. At 1–10 p.p.m. silver salmon did not appear to be affected, but a 20 p.p.m. solution gave an 80 per cent kill in 22 h.

(5) 'Sterox–SK.' This detergent is stated to be similar in properties to 'Sterox–SE'. The experiments showed it to be rather more toxic. The reactions of the fish to both 'Sterox' preparations were similar; they showed little sign of irritation, but became progressively weaker and lingered a long time before death. It is pointed out that this is an unfavourable feature as affected fish would attract no attention and would quietly settle to the bottom and die.

Apart from the observation that fish display respiratory distress in toxic concentrations of synthetic detergents little information seems to have been gathered about the nature of their effects on fish. Surface-active agents are said to precipitate or denature proteins and to

124

inactivate viruses. Their germicidal property has been known for some time and does not seem to be related to their ability to denature proteins, nor is it due to their ability to lower surface tension. In some way they depress the metabolism of bacteria and it has been suggested that they act on the cell membranes of micro-organisms in such a way as to cause the loss of enzymes and co-enzymes[11]. Schmid and Mann[12] have described changes induced in the gills of the trout by the detergent sodium dodecylbenzenesulphonate (DBS). They found that a 5 p.p.m. solution causes the respiratory folds of the laminae to stick together, and there is a loss of the mucous cells. Higher concentrations of the detergent bring about an increasing destruction of the respiratory epithelium; a 20 p.p.m. solution has a very marked effect in 1 h, with the production of multiple haematomas. The damage to the respiratory organs results in a diminished uptake of oxygen and in impairment of the salt balance.

The natural detergents, or soaps, do not appear to have created any major fish toxicity problems, but some of the investigators who have worked on the toxicity of synthetic detergents to fish have also tested the effects of soaps for comparative purposes. Leclerc and Devlaminck[5] found that sodium palmitate, sodium oleate and sodium stearate were toxic to minnows (*Phoxinus*) down to concentrations of 10–12 p.p.m. in distilled water. Solutions in hard water were much less toxic, the limiting concentrations being 250–300 p.p.m. for sodium stearate and 900–1,000 p.p.m. for the other two soaps. They noted that high concentrations of soaps, much above the lethal level, appeared to damage the respiratory epithelium, their corroding effect being marked by the appearance of threads of blood. At the minimum lethal dose in distilled water death appeared to be due to a lowering of the surface tension, but at the minimum lethal dose in hard water death could be attributed to obstruction of the gills by flakes of calcium soap, and excessive alkalinity. The fish displayed symptoms of respiratory distress, the body became covered with a thick coat of mucus; at death the mouth was open and the gill covers were raised.

Henderson, Pickering and Cohen[9] tested the toxicity of three packaged household soaps to fathead minnows, and these proved rather more toxic than entire packaged detergents in soft water, but were very much less toxic in hard water. The average 96 h TL_m for the soaps in soft water was 34 p.p.m. against 61 p.p.m. for the detergents. It is interesting to note that when pure sodium stearate was tested the 96 h TL_m was found to be 100 p.p.m., which suggests that the packaged soaps contained a much more toxic kind of soap, or some other harmful ingredients.

The available information on the effects of synthetic detergents on fish seems to show that while some types, the alkyl benzene sulphonates in particular, have a moderately high degree of toxicity, none, so far, has been found to have a lethal potential comparable with the cyanides, the heavy metals, and the more toxic insecticides. Nevertheless, the widespread and increasing use of these reagents makes it necessary for the position to be kept under review. It is possible, of course, that pollution by detergents may have some indirect, harmful effect on fish, brought about by depletion of the flora and invertebrate fauna. A study of the River Lee by Hynes and Roberts[13] has been published recently. The work covered the period October 1950 to September 1961 and during this period the detergent content of the effluent from the sewage works at Luton, which accounts for most of the flow of the river in its first 16 miles, rose to 4 p.p.m. and later declined to rather less than 2 p.p.m. These changes appeared to be accompanied by very little change in the biological condition of the river, whose fauna includes a considerable variety of invertebrates, and minnows and sticklebacks.

REFERENCES

[1] Metropolitan Water Board. Report on discharge of synthetic detergents to rivers with special reference to the R. Lee. *Surveyor, Lond.*, 112 (1953) 73

[2] Schmassmann, H. Ueber die Giftwirkung von härtebeständigen Waschmitteln auf Fische. *Schweiz. FischZtg.*, 54 (1946) 283–9

[3] Oldham, L. W. A study of the effect of non-ionic detergents on the purification of domestic sewage. Undated. I.C.I.

[4] Degens, P. N., Van der Zee, H., Kommer, J. D. and Kamphuis, A. H. Synthetic detergents and sewage processing. V. The effect of synthetic detergents on certain water fauna. *J. Inst. Sew. Purif.*, 1 (1950) 63–8

[5] Leclerc, E. and Devlaminck, F. Les détergents naturels ou synthétiques et les poissons. *Bull. du C.B.E.D.E.*, No. 17 (1952) 165–71

[6] Ministry of Housing and Local Government. Report of the Committee on Synthetic Detergents. 1956. London; H.M.S.O.

[7] Herbert, D. W. M., Elkins, G. H. J., Mann, H. T. and Hemens, J. Toxicity of synthetic detergents to rainbow trout. *Wat. Waste Treatm. J.*, 6 (1957) 394–7

[8] *Water Pollution Research, 1956.* 1957. London; H.M.S.O.

[9] Henderson, C., Pickering, Q. H. and Cohen, J. M. The toxicity of synthetic detergents and soaps to fish. *Sewage industr. Wastes*, 31 (1959) 295–306

[10] Holland, G. A., Lasater, J. E., Neuman, E. D. and Eldridge, W. E. Toxic effects of organic and inorganic pollutants on young salmon and trout. *St. Wash. Dept. Fish. Res. Bull.* No. 5, (1960)

[11] Goodman, L. S. and Gilman, A. *The Pharmacological Basis of Therapeutics*, 2nd edn. 1955. New York; Macmillan

[12] Schmid, O. J. and Mann, H. Action of a detergent (dodecylbenzene-sulphonate) on the gills of the trout. *Nature, Lond.*, 192 (1961) 675

[13] Hynes, H. B. N. and Roberts, F. W. The biological effects of synthetic detergents in the River Lee, Hertfordshire. *Ann. appl. Biol.*, 50 (1962) 779–90

11

INSECTICIDES AND HERBICIDES

INSECTICIDES have been used in increasing quantities in the past 60 years, and compounds of different type have succeeded one another in popularity. At the beginning of the century the main types available were arsenic compounds, lime-sulphur, petroleum oils and nicotine. Between World War I and World War II fluorine compounds, pyrethrum and derris were added and a number of synthetic organic materials, such as the thiocyanates and the dinitro- compounds made their appearance. During this time the possibility that insecticides might be responsible for water pollution seems to have attracted very little attention, though a few papers concerning the toxicity of insecticides to fish appeared, such as that of Chevalier[1] dealing with pyrethrum. Two factors probably account for this. Prior to World War II insect control was not carried out on the scale seen today, and the insecticides then in use appear to be much less lethal to fish than modern types. Arsenic, though known to be toxic to nearly all forms of life, does not appear to be particularly toxic to fish. Surber[2] showed that sodium arsenite can be used to control vegetation in fish-ponds and that a concentration of 1·743 p.p.m. (as As_2O_3) does not appear to be harmful to the fish. Brown[3] states that sodium arsenite is non-toxic to fish at 4 p.p.m. and a recent study by Alderdice and Brett[4] gives the 48 h median tolerance limit for young chum salmon as 11 p.p.m. As_2O_3. Grindley[5] found that minnows lived over 36 h in solutions containing 17·8 p.p.m. of arsenic. Nicotine is so volatile that there is little probability of danger to fish arising from its use. Little evidence seems to be available regarding the toxicity to fish of the dinitro- compounds. According to Rudd and Genelly[6] there is no evidence of wildlife mortality in California due to the use of DNOC as an insecticide or herbicide. However, DNOCHP used in Egypt at 3–5 p.p.m. to control mollusca acting as schistosome vectors killed all the fish in the treated waters[7]. Grindley has shown that the limiting concentration of dinitrophenol for minnows is about 30 p.p.m.[5]. Of the older insecticides derris is probably the most toxic to fish and its effectiveness as a fish poison has been known for centuries. Its active ingredient, rotenone, is said to enter the body by way of the gills, to act as a paralytic nerve poison. In insects it works as a respiratory depressant, but whether it has this effect on fish does not appear to have been tested. Goldfish are killed in 6 h by rotenone at a concentration of 0·027 p.p.m.[3], and in amounts up to 0·5 p.p.m. it can be used as a fish poison to control fish populations[6]. Lower concentrations can be effective in the selective removal of different species. Its action can be counteracted by potassium permanganate, which will oxidize it to a non-toxic compound, but care must be taken not to use an excess of permanganate as this is also a fish poison; 2–2·5 p.p.m. will neutralize 0·05 p.p.m. of rotenone[8].

After World War II DDT began to be used extensively as an insecticide, and though many new chlorinated hydrocarbons and many new insecticides of other types have been produced, it remains one of the best known and widely used of chemicals for insect control. In 1944 the U.S.A. produced about 4,500 tons of DDT, in 1955 this had increased to over 50,000 tons. It is estimated that over 3,000 tons of DDT was used in California in 1951. It was soon discovered that it is very toxic to fish. One of the first to note this was Pielou[9] who tested the effect of DDT dissolved in paraffin on the Kafue bream (*Tilapia kafuensis*) of Rhodesia. Even at a dilution of 1/72,000,000 the survival time was only 4–5 days and at 1/36,000,000 none of the fish survived 2 days. One of the most important of the early studies of the toxicity of DDT to fish is that of Langford[10]. Langford produced very fine suspensions by adding to water various amounts of an alcoholic solution of DDT, which caused it to separate out in particles sufficiently small to remain in permanent suspension. Experiments were carried out with creek chub, redbelly dace, common suckers and speckled trout. At 0·1 p.p.m. the suspensions were fatal to all four species in under 13 h, at 0·05 p.p.m. the survival times ranged from 6 to 20 h, and at 0·01 p.p.m. from 7 to 55 h. The speckled trout appeared to be particularly sensitive; the average survival time of fry was only 9·5 h at 0·005 p.p.m. and 0·001 p.p.m. was fatal to yearlings, in several days. Langford concluded that the DDT threshold for speckled trout yearlings and creek chub is 0·005–0·01 p.p.m.; for the common sucker, about 0·001 p.p.m.; for speckled trout fry, below 0·001 p.p.m. The tests were carried out with fine suspensions as the true solubility of DDT in water is extremely low, about 0·0002 p.p.m. according to Brown[3]. Langford also tested the effect of emulsions of a cyclohexanone solution of the insecticide, of surface films of oily solutions, of food containing DDT, and the injection of DDT–oil solution into the peritoneal cavity. In most cases the fish were killed; death in all cases was accompanied by erratic, uncoordinated swimming movement and spasms, followed by loss of equilibrium, with longer and longer periods of quiescence until respiratory movements ceased.

Most other investigators, though not all, have confirmed the high toxicity of DDT to fish. Thus Gagnon[11] has shown that the lethal limit for the Atlantic salmon is about 0·07 p.p.m., and Hatch[12] found that its survival time at 0·08 p.p.m. is only 36 h. Some further data will be found in Table 9, and in the discussion of comparative studies of insecticides. When fish are exposed to DDT poisoning the time factor appears to be very important; provided the exposure time is short they may be able to survive comparatively high concentrations. Arnason *et al.*[13] carried out some experiments on the control of *Simulium* (black-fly) larvae by means of DDT in the Saskatchewan river. The river was treated by spraying from aircraft a 12 per cent solution of DDT with alkylnaphthalene solvent, emulsifier and red dye. The treated water travelled down the river and samples taken 5 miles downstream showed that it passed the sampling point in about an hour, the concentration of insecticide reaching a maximum of 0·085 p.p.m. in midstream. A virtually complete disappearance of the black-fly larvae resulted but fish confined in cages a short distance downstream from the sprayed area were not affected. Several species were tested; laboratory tests were carried out with three types, not named, but no harmful effects were seen at 25, 30 and 50 p.p.m. DDT but the exposure period in these experiments was only 30 min. It was concluded that the application of sufficient DDT to give a concentration of not less than 0·1 p.p.m. for a period of half an hour or more will give a satisfactory control of black-fly larvae, and that this amount is harmless to fish. It will be noted that in this case the insecticide was sprayed in the form of an emulsion which mixed with the water. This was necessary because the black-fly larvae live attached to stones on the bottom. It is possible that when it is applied in this way DDT is less dangerous than when it is applied as a surface film. In an oily surface film it is particularly dangerous to fish that have a habit of breaking the surface. Langford[10] found that this was apparently the cause of death in the case of the creek chub, as the mouths and gills of the fish became contaminated with the toxic solution.

A voluminous literature has accumulated on the toxicity of DDT to many kinds of animals, particularly insects and man. The primary site of the lethal action of DDT in insects is the nervous system and the nature of the action appears to be an unstabilizing effect similar to that produced by a lack of calcium ions. In mammals the central nervous system is affected, the first symptom of DDT poisoning being tremor of the skeletal muscles.

More insecticides of the chlorinated-hydrocarbon type were soon produced after the success of DDT and comparative studies of their toxicity to fish appeared in the literature. Lawrence[14] used fingerling bluegills and largemouth bass in experiments in which DDT, toxaphene, chlordane and BHC were added to ponds and aquaria. Chlordane proved to be the least toxic and toxaphene the most toxic. Mayhew[15] used rainbow trout; the insecticides tested were DDT, chlordane, heptachlor, methoxychlor, aldrin, toxaphene and dieldrin. The lowest concentrations giving a 100 per cent kill in 24 h were determined; these were: DDT and chlordane, 0.5 p.p.m.; heptachlor, 0·25; methoxychlor, aldrin, dieldrin and toxaphene, 0·05 p.p.m. These figures are concentrations of active insecticidal ingredient in solutions made with emulsifiable concentrates. Some of the insecticides were also tested as dusts and wettable powders.

Mayhew observed symptoms similar to those seen by Langford in his experiments with DDT. The fish displayed marked irritability, being very sensitive to vibrations and swimming in a wild fashion when the side of the aquarium was tapped. Later there was a loss of equilibrium, with muscular spasms and convulsions. A marked feature was blanching of the integument caused by contraction of the chromatophores. The high toxicity of toxaphene to fish was confirmed by Hemphill[16] who tried it out as a fish poison, and found that 0·1 p.p.m. applied to lakes as a dust or emulsified solution would give a total kill of carp in 72 h. Stringer and McMynn[17] also tried toxaphene as a fish poison. They treated 8 lakes in British Columbia with toxaphene at concentrations ranging from 0·01 to 0·1 p.p.m. and most of the fish were killed at all concentrations within 120 h. The compound showed an extremely high degree of persistence, for it was found that 9 months after the treatment no fish could be netted in the lakes, and tests with fish in cages showed that the water was still toxic.

Persistence of toxic properties is one of the main characteristics of the chlorinated hydrocarbon insecticides, but in water they appear to vary somewhat in this respect. Bridges[18] studied a pond which was contaminated with endrin in the summer. The water, mud, fish and aquatic vegetation were analysed from time to time to find out how long the endrin remained. No measurable amounts remained in the water after one month or in the mud after two months. It disappeared from the vegetation in less than two months but residues remained in the fish for about three months. Endrin is one of the most toxic of the chlorinated hydrocarbon insecticides. Katz[19] finds that the 96 h median tolerance limit for coho salmon is as low as 0·0005 p.p.m., and according to unpublished data cited by Rudd and Genelly[6] the limiting concentration for bass, bluegills and goldfish is only 0·0003 p.p.m. No substance so far tested appears to have a higher toxicity to fish.

Another chlorinated hydrocarbon insecticide of major importance is dieldrin, whose toxicity to fish is the subject of an investigation by Tarzwell and Henderson[20]. There are some particularly interesting points about this study. A survival curve (*Figure 49*) was worked out for fathead minnows; plotted on logarithmic time and concentration scales the graph is linear over the concentration range 0·03–0·3 p.p.m.; a threshold seems to be reached at about 0·02 p.p.m., and above 0·56 p.p.m. an increase in the concentration seems to bring about no shortening of the overturning time.

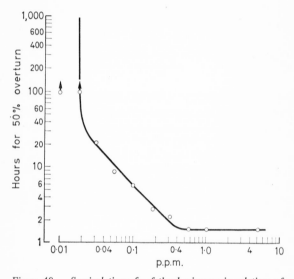

Figure 49.   Survival times for fathead minnows in solutions of dieldrin.   Temperature 22° C

(Drawn from the data of Tarzwell and Henderson[20].)

The survival curve was used for bio-assay determinations of the dieldrin content of run-off water from areas treated with this insecticide, and it was found that the dieldrin content could be estimated within 25 per cent.   Run-off water from a 7·14 acre, dieldrin-treated area, partly grass and partly built upon, was collected and its toxicity to fish determined.   Samples taken after the first rain following treatment were toxic to the fathead minnows at a dilution of about 1 in 2, and some fish died in water collected after the third rain, but the mortality was less than 50 per cent.   Dieldrin is a stereoisomer of endrin.

BHC or benzene hexachloride is rather less important than DDT. Though it is an extremely powerful insecticide its uses are much more limited owing to its tendency to impart an unpleasant odour and flavour to plants. It is produced by the chlorination of benzene in the presence of light. There are various possible positions for the hydrogen and chlorine atoms in the molecule, and so the compound exists in a number of different isomers which are remarkably different in their degree of toxicity. The γ-isomer is one of the most toxic of all insecticides whereas the β- and ϵ-isomers are practically non-toxic to insects. The δ-isomer is moderately active but variable in its effects on different insects, and is the most toxic isomer to snails. The original wettable powder preparation called BHC or 666 contained 6–12 per cent of the γ-isomer. Newer preparations contain a much higher proportion, and the wettable powders and emulsifiable concentrates sold under the name Lindane, which replaces the old name Gammexane, contain not less than 99 per cent of the γ-isomer. The insecticide has been used for the control of flies in percolating filters[21] and the possibility that some might be washed out with the effluent, and so reach a river, led to a study of its toxicity to rainbow trout[22]. A preparation called Gammexane dispersible powder P520 was used for the tests and it was found that at concentrations below 5 p.p.m. the toxicity fell off very rapidly, so that at 0·77 p.p.m. less than 50 per cent of the fish died in 81 days. The preparation P520, however, contains only 6·5 per cent of the γ-isomer of BHC.

The most comprehensive study of the chlorinated-hydrocarbon insecticides is that of Henderson, Pickering and Tarzwell[23]. The preparations tested were aldrin, dieldrin, endrin, chlordane, heptachlor, toxaphene, methoxychlor, DDT, lindane and technical BHC. The fish tested were fathead minnows, bluegills, goldfish and guppies. Median tolerance limits were determined for 24, 48 and 96 h, in most cases for soft water, but with the fathead minnows limits were also determined for a hard water. This was a natural limestone water obtained directly from springs; the soft water was prepared in the laboratory by mixing 95 parts of demineralized distilled water with 5 parts of spring water.

The bluegills proved to be the most sensitive of the fish tested. The most resistant, in some cases, were the goldfish, in others, the guppies. The tolerance limits for the bluegills, in soft water, are shown in *Figure 50*. It will be seen that endrin is very definitely the most toxic insecticide of the group, and BHC the least toxic. When tolerance limits for BHC based on the γ-isomer content are compared with those for lindane (100 per cent in the preparation used) it is found that they are very different; about 10 times higher for bluegills and nearly 40 times higher for fathead minnows. They should be about the same if the ingredients of BHC other than the γ-isomer are inert. It appears that the other isomers of benzene hexachloride in technical BHC depress the toxicity of the γ-isomer in some way. Additional experiments served to confirm this. Lindane at 0·1 p.p.m. gave a 100 per cent kill of fathead minnows in 24 h; when 3·2 p.p.m. of BHC and 0·1 p.p.m. of lindane were added to the same test tank no fish died in a 96 h test. A concentration of 3·2 p.p.m. of technical BHC alone produced no fish mortality.

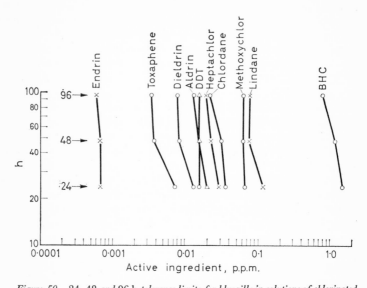

Figure 50. 24, 48 *and* 96 h *tolerance limits for bluegills in solutions of chlorinated hydrocarbon insecticides. Concentrations are* p.p.m. *of active ingredient; in the case of BHC, the* γ-*isomer. Temperature* 25° C

(Drawn from the data of Henderson, Pickering and Tarzwell[23].)

The physiological reactions of the test fish were somewhat similar for all the compounds tested except BHC. Even at the higher concentrations the first effects were not apparent until after 30–60 min exposure, and at low concentrations much longer times were required. The main symptoms, when they appeared, were excitement, jerky movements resulting from muscular spasms, loss of equilibrium, swelling of the abdominal region of the body, and blanching of the integument. In BHC the fish did not react in this way but sank slowly to the bottom of the aquarium where they gradually expired. The tests with fathead minnows carried out with hard and soft water showed that within the range tested the pH, alkalinity and hardness of the water had no major effect on the toxicity of any of the 10 compounds.

Another group of modern insecticides is formed by the organic phosphates. Parathion is, perhaps, the best known of this type; others are malathion, guthion, EPN, TEPP, chlorthion, disyston, dipterex, OMPA, para-oxon, systox and co-ral. Some insecticides of this type have a very high degree of toxicity to man. The use of parathion for control measures requires protective clothing and a respirator.

Henderson, Pickering and Tarzwell[23, 24] have compared the toxicity of the organic phosphorus insecticides to fish with that of the chlorinated hydrocarbons and have shown that the phosphorus compounds are much less toxic. Of the various types tested EPN and para-oxon were the most toxic, but for both of these the 96 h tolerance limit for fathead minnows, at 0·25 p.p.m., is much higher than the corresponding values for all the chlorinated hydrocarbons except BHC. Another factor making them less dangerous to fish is their inferior stability in water; most of them hydrolyse rapidly to non-toxic products.

It has been shown that the organic phosphate insecticides have an inactivating effect on acetylcholinesterase in the nervous system of fish[25] and thus depress or inhibit the transmission of nerve impulses. The rapidity with which they take effect, and the rapidity with which recovery takes place by reactivation of the acetylcholinesterase on removal of the toxic substance, varies considerably. With malathion, inhibition and recovery are rapid; exposure to parathion for the same period results in a much smaller degree of inhibition but recovery is extremely slow and fish may die many days after removal from contaminated water.

Organic phosphate preparations have been used for fly control in drainage systems and Hoffman[26] has carried out some tests to determine whether the resulting effluents are a danger to trout. He found that parathion in concentrations up to 1 p.p.m. appeared to be harmless to speckled trout and rainbow trout. Dipterex also appeared to be perfectly safe at 1 p.p.m. and 10 p.p.m. However Matsue, Endo and Tabata[27], in a study of the effect of parathion on goldfish and the Japanese killifish, found that prolonged exposure to concentrations well below the lethal level resulted in retarded growth, as less food was eaten. Harmful effects were evident at a concentration 1/30 of the 48 h median tolerance limit.

In a general review of their work on the toxicity of insecticides to fish, Henderson, Pickering and Tarzwell[23, 24] have pointed out that the problem of insect control without excessive damage to certain land or water uses is not insurmountable, but that it will require more attention, and that extensive laboratory and field research is needed in such categories as the development of selective toxicants and methods and timing of application to provide for minimum effects on fish and wildlife. Thus it is accepted that run-off from areas treated with insecticides is a hazard to fish, but little is known about the way this is influenced by the soil type, land cover, rainfall intensity and frequency, organic content and turbidity of the water.

Lethal limits for fish, collected from the literature, are given in Table 9. In most cases the figures are median tolerance limits; how fast the toxicity falls off at concentrations below these values is not

Table 9.   Lethal Limits for Insecticides*

Insecticide	Fish tested	Concentration (p.p.m.)	Exposure time (hours)	Ref.
Aldrin . .	bluegill	0·013	96	24
,, . .	fathead minnow	0.033	96	24
,, . .	goldfish	0·028	96	24
,, . .	guppy	0·033	96	24
,, . .	rainbow trout	0·05	24	15
BHC . .	bluegill	0·79	96	24
,, . .	fathead minnow	2.3	96	24
,, . .	goldfish	2·3	96	24
,, . .	guppy	2·17	96	24
Chlordane .	channel cat	0·5	96	32
,,	fathead minnow	0·052	96	24
,,	goldfish	0·082	96	24
,,	guppy	0·19	96	24
,,	rainbow trout	0·5	24	15
Chlorothion .	fathead minnow	3·2	96	24
Co-ral . .	bluegill	0·18	96	24
DDD . .	channel cat	<2·6	96	32
DDT . .	bluegill	0·016	96	24
,, . .	channel cat	>1·0	96	32
,, . .	fathead minnow	0·032	96	24
,, . .	goldfish	0·027	96	24
,, . .	guppy	0·043	96	24
,, . .	rainbow trout	0·5	24	15
,, . .	,, ,,	0·032	36	12
,, . .	salmon	0·08	36	12
,, . .	,,	0·072	?	11
,, . .	speckled trout	0·032	36	12
Dieldrin . .	bluegill	0·0079	96	24
,, . .	channel cat	<2·5	96	32

* In this table the concentration values cited from References 19, 24 and 32 are median tolerance limits. In other cases the concentrations are the lowest at which definite toxic effect is indicated by the data. Most of the experiments were carried out at temperatures of 19–25° C. The works cited should be consulted for the chemical names of the compounds, and the methods employed for making the test solutions.

Table 9—cont.

Insecticide	Fish tested	Concentration (p.p.m.)	Exposure time (hours)	Ref.
Dieldrin . .	fathead minnow	0·016	96	24
,, . .	goldfish	0·037	96	24
,, . .	guppy	0·022	96	24
,, . .	rainbow trout	0·05	24	15
Dilan . .	channel cat	<0·5	96	32
Dipterex .	fathead minnow	180·0	96	24
Di-syston .	bluegill	0·064	96	24
Endrin . .	bluegill	0·0006	96	24
,, . .	coho salmon	0·0005	96	19
,, . .	fathead minnow	0·001	96	24
,, . .	goldfish	0·0019	96	24
,, . .	guppy	0·0015	96	24
EPN . .	fathead minnow	0·2	96	24
Guthion . .	bluegill	0·0052	96	24
,, . .	fathead minnow	0·093	96	24
Heptachlor .	bluegill	0·019	96	24
,,	channel cat	0·175	96	32
,,	fathead minnow	0·094	96	24
,,	goldfish	0·23	96	24
,,	guppy	0·107	96	24
,,	rainbow trout	0·25	24	15
Lindane .	bluegill	0·077	96	24
,, . .	fathead minnow	0·062	96	24
,, . .	goldfish	0·152	96	24
,, . .	guppy	0·138	96	24
Malathion .	channel cat	13·05	96	32
,,	fathead minnow	12·5	96	24
Methoxychlor .	bluegill	0·062	96	24
,,	fathead minnow	0·064	96	24
,,	goldfish	0·056	96	24
,,	guppy	0·12	96	24
,,	rainbow trout	0·05	24	15
OMPA . .	fathead minnow	121·0	96	24
Para-oxon .	,, ,,	0·33	96	24
Parathion .	,, ,,	1·4–2·7	96	24
Sevin . .	bluegill	5·5	96	24
,, . .	fathead minnow	12·0	96	24
Systox . .	,, ,,	3·6	96	24
TEPP . .	channel cat	1·6	96	32
,, . .	fathead minnow	1·7	96	24
Toxaphene .	bluegill	0·0035	96	24
,, .	carp	0·1	?	16
,, .	goldfish	0·0056	96	24
,, .	guppy	0·043	96	24
,, .	rainbow trout	0·05	24	15

known, for in the case of fish there is very little information available on the survival time–concentration relationship of insecticides. It will be noted that the lethal limits cover a very wide concentration range, from 180 p.p.m. for dipterex down to 0·0005 p.p.m. for endrin.

Herbicides may contaminate rivers and streams in a number of ways.   Like insecticides they may be present in run-off from treated land, they may reach streams in spray drift, and spraying equipment may be cleaned in waterways.   Many herbicides are now used for the control of aquatic vegetation.   The chief studies on the toxicity of herbicides to fish are those of Davis and Hardcastle[28], who used bluegills and largemouth bass; Bond, Lewis and Fryer[29], who used largemouth bass, chinook and coho salmon, and Alabaster[30] who used rainbow trout.   Table 10 gives a list of the substances tested and 48 h median tolerance limits for these fish.   On a p.p.m. basis herbicides are generally much less toxic to fish than insecticides, but for the control of aquatic vegetation they have to be employed in rather high concentrations which may be near the danger level for fish.   Thus the TL_m values for 2,4-D given by Davis and Hardcastle for bluegills and largemouth bass are 375 and 350 p.p.m.; application at a concentration of 100 p.p.m. is required to give a partial control of aquatic vegetation[31] and much higher concentrations are required for complete control.

Table 10.   48 h Median Tolerance Limits for Herbicides*

Herbicide	Fish tested	48 h TL_m (p.p.m.)	Temp. °C
2,3,5-TBA . . .	bluegill	90	25
„ . . .	largemouth bass	55	25
2,3,6-TBA . . .	bluegill	1,750	25
„ . . .	largemouth bass	1,250	25
2,4-D . . .	bluegill	375	25
„ . . .	largemouth bass	350	25
4-(MCPB) . . .	bluegill	15	25
„ . . .	largemouth bass	10	25
4-(2,4-DB) . . .	bluegill	8	25
„ . . .	largemouth bass	10	25
ACP-M-569 .	chinook salmon	155	20
Aminotriazole . .	coho salmon	325	20
„ . .	largemouth bass	>1,000	20
Baron	chinook salmon	2·3	20
„ . . .	channel cat	6·9	19
C 56	bluegill	30	25
„	largemouth bass	35	25
Chlorax . . .	rainbow trout	1,800	18
„ . . .	channel cat	2,367	20
Chlorea . . .	rainbow trout	1,100	18
CIPC	bluegill	12	25
„	largemouth bass	10	25

* Based on the data of Davis and Hardcastle[28]; Bond, Lewis and Fryer[29]; Alabaster[30], and Clemens and Sneed[32].

Table 10—cont.

Herbicide	Fish tested	48 h TL_m (p.p.m.)	Temp. °C
Diquat . . .	chinook salmon	28·5	20
Diuron . . .	coho salmon	16	20
Dowpon . . .	,, ,,	340	20
,, . .	brown trout	210	18
EDB . . •. .	bluegill	18	25
,, ...	largemouth bass	15	25
Endothal . . .	,, ,,	200	25
. . .	chinook salmon	136	25
F-98 (Acrolein) . .	,, ,,	0·08*	20
Hyamine 1622 . .	coho salmon	53	20
Kuron . . .	chinook salmon	1·23	20
Monuron . . .	coho salmon	110	20
Nemagon . . .	bluegill	20	25
,, . .	largemouth bass	20	25
Omazene . . .	chinook salmon	0·83	20
Phygon XL . . .	largemouth bass	0·07	20
. . .	channel cat	0·14	19
Shell D 50 . .	rainbow trout	210	18
Simazine . . .	chinook salmon	6·6	20
,, . .	rainbow trout	85	18
Sodium TCA . .	chinook salmon	> 870	20
TCA	channel cat	> 2,000	20

* This value is for 24 h, no figure for 48 h is given in the data.

REFERENCES

[1] Chevalier, J. Le pyrèthre (chrysanthème insecticide). Activité pharmacodynamique et thérapeutique. *Bull. sci. pharmacol.*, 37 (1930) 154–65

[2] Surber, E. W. Controlling vegetation in fish ponds with sodium arsenite. *U.S. Bur. Fish., Invest., Rep.* No. 11 (1932) 39 pp.

[3] Brown, A. W. A. *Insect Control by Chemicals.* 1951. New York; John Wiley. London; Chapman and Hall

[4] Alderdice, D. F. and Brett, J. R. Toxicity of sodium arsenite to young chum salmon. *Progress Rep. Pacific Coast Stations, Fish. Res. Bd. Can.*, No. 108 (1957) 27–9

[5] Grindley, J. Toxicity to rainbow trout and minnows of some substances known to be present in waste water discharged to rivers. *Ann. appl. Biol.*, 33 (1946) 103–12

[6] Rudd, R. L. and Genelly, R. E. Pesticides: their use and toxicity in relation to wild life. *Calif. Fish and Game, Game Bull.*, No. 7, Davis, 1956

[7] Kuntz, R. E. and Wells, W. H. Laboratory and field evaluations of two dinitrophenols as molluscacides for control of schistosome vectors in Egypt with emphasis on importance of temperature. *Amer. J. trop. Med.*, 31 (1951) 784–824

[8] Lawrence, J. M. Preliminary results on the use of potassium permanganate to counter the effects of rotenone on fish. *Progr. Fish Cult.*, 18 (1956) 15–21

⁹ Pielou, D. P.   Lethal effects of DDT on young fish.   *Nature, Lond.*, 158 (1946) 378

¹⁰ Langford, R. R.   The effect of DDT on freshwater fishes.   In *Forest Spraying and Some Effects of DDT, Dept. Lands Forests Ontario Canada, Div. Res. Biol. Bull.*, 2 (1949) 19–37

¹¹ Gagnon, A.   La toxicitée du DDT pour le saumon de l'Atlantique (*Salmo salar* Linné) et les alevins de truite (*Salvelinus fontinalis* Mitchell). *Canad. J. Zool.*, 36 (1958) 479–87

¹² Hatch, R. W.   Relative sensitivity of salmonids to DDT.   *Progr. Fish Cult.*, 19 (1957) 89–91

¹³ Arnason, A. P., Brown, A. W. A., Fredeen, F. J. H., Hopewell, W. W. and Rempel, J. G.   Experiments in the control of *Simulium arcticum* Malloch by means of DDT in the Saskatchewan river.   *Sci. Agric.*, 29 (1949) 527–37

¹⁴ Lawrence, J. M.   Toxicity of some new insecticides to several species of pondfish.   *Progr. Fish Cult.*, 12 (1950) 141–6

¹⁵ Mayhew, J.   Toxicity of seven different insecticides to rainbow trout, *Salmo gairdnerii* Richardson.   *Proc. Iowa Acad. Sci.*, 62 (1955) 599–606

¹⁶ Hemphill, J. E.   Toxaphene as a fish poison.   *Progr. Fish Cult.*, 16 (1954) 41–2

¹⁷ Stringer, G. E. and McMynn, R. G.   Experiments with toxaphene as a fish poison.   *Canad. Fish Cult.*, 23 (1958) 39–47

¹⁸ Bridges, W. R.   Disappearance of endrin from fish and other materials of a pond environment.   *Trans. Amer. Fish. Soc.*, 90 (1961) 332–4

¹⁹ Katz, M.   Acute toxicity of some organic insecticides to three species of salmonids and to the threespine stickleback.   *Trans. Amer. Fish. Soc.*, 90 (1961) 264–8

²⁰ Tarzwell, C. M. and Henderson, C.   Toxicity of dieldrin to fish.   *Trans. Amer. Fish. Soc.*, 86 (1956) 245–57

²¹ *Water Pollution Research, 1949.*   1950.   London; H.M.S.O.

²² *Water Pollution Research, 1953.*   1954.   London; H.M.S.O.

²³ Henderson, C., Pickering, Q. H. and Tarzwell, C. M.   Relative toxicity of ten chlorinated hydrocarbon insecticides to four species of fish. *Trans. Amer. Fish. Soc.*, 88 (1959) 23–32

²⁴ Henderson, C., Pickering, Q. H. and Tarzwell, C. M.   The toxicity of organic phosphorus and chlorinated hydrocarbon insecticides to fish. In *Biological Problems in Water Pollution, Trans. 1959 Seminar Robert A. Taft Sanit. Eng. Cent. Tech. Rep. W60-3*, Cincinnati, 1960

²⁵ Weiss, C. M.   Response of fish to sub-lethal exposures of organic phosphorus insecticides.   *Sewage industr. Wastes*, 31 (1959) 580–93

²⁶ Hoffman, R. A.   Toxicity of three phosphorus insecticides to cold water game fish.   *Mosquito News*, 17 (1957) 213

²⁷ Matsue, Y., Endo, T. and Tabata, K.   Effect of an insecticide, parathion, on aquatic animals at lower ranges than its lethal concentration. *Bull. Jap. Soc. sci. Fish.*, 23 (1957) 358–62

²⁸ Davis, J. T. and Hardcastle, W. S.   Biological assay of herbicides for fish toxicity.   *Weeds*, 7 (1959) 397–404

²⁹ Bond, C. E., Lewis, R. H. and Fryer, J. L.   Toxicity of various herbicidal materials to fishes.   In *Biological Problems in Water Pollution, Trans. 1959 Seminar Robert A. Taft Sanit. Eng. Cent. Tech. Rep. W60-3*, Cincinnati, 1960

³⁰ Alabaster, J. S.   Toxicity of weedkillers, algicides and fungicides to trout.   *Proc. 4th Brit. Weed Control Conf.*, (1960) 1–2

INSECTICIDES AND HERBICIDES

31 Gerking, S. D.   Destruction of submerged aquatic plants by 2,4-D. *J. Wildlife Mgmt*, 12 (1948) 221–7
32 Clemens, H. P. and Sneed, K. E.   Lethal doses of several commercial chemicals for fingerling channel catfish. *Fish. Bull. U.S.*, No. 316, Washington, 1959

12

PHENOL AND OTHER SUBSTANCES
ASSOCIATED WITH TAR AND GAS WASTES

THE distillation of coal for the production of gas, coke and the tarry materials used for the manufacture of dyes and organic chemicals results in a watery waste known as ammoniacal gas liquor, and the disposal of this is a cause of pollution. Ammoniacal gas liquor contains free ammonia, ammonium salts, cyanide, sulphide, thiocyanate, and a variety of aromatic compounds including pyridine, phenols, cresols and xylenols. After treatment to remove ammonia the waste is called 'spent gas liquor', and phenol, or carbolic acid, is the most abundant of its many phenolic constituents[1,2], and probably the most dangerous to fish. Phenolic substances are also present in materials for road surfacing, in sheep dips and many industrial wastes such as those associated with the manufacture of plastics, dyes and disinfectants[3]. Gas liquor, discharged untreated to a stream, has an extremely high oxygen demand, many times greater than that of sewage[3].

As various benzene derivatives are now used so extensively for insect and weed control there has been a considerable study of their pharmacology. Benzene is said to be practically non-toxic as a stomach poison or contact spray to insects[4] but many elements and radicals can be introduced into the benzene ring to give a great variety of toxic substances. Thus the conversion of benzene into phenol by the introduction of a hydroxyl group increases its toxicity 5–10 times and the substitution of a nitro group to form nitrobenzene $C_6H_5NO_2$ increases the toxicity 100 times. Chlorination gives the insecticide BHC and the introduction of a CH_3, an OH and two NO_2 groups gives dinitro-ortho-cresol or DNOC.

Shelford[5] was one of the first to study the effects of gas waste upon fish. Most of his experimental work was carried out with the small sunfish, *Lepomis humilis*, but many other species were used for comparative purposes. The waste used in the various tests was what is known as the 'drip', the water accumulating in the bottom of the gas-holders, in the pipes leading to and from them. This waste was found to be toxic to fish but the effect of different samples varied greatly, some samples being 10 or 12 times as toxic as others. The amount of tarry material present appeared to be important and the most toxic samples contained much tar. Shelford obtained analyses of the waste and tested the effect of its various constituents on sunfish; the criterion adopted was the concentration in p.p.m. fatal to the fish in 1 h. His results are given in Table 11. It will be seen that the different substances tested vary considerably in their degree of toxicity, some normally considered insoluble in water, such as naphthalene, are very poisonous.

Table 11. The Toxicity of Substances Occurring in Tar and Gas Wastes to Sunfish (*Lepomis humilis*) and Perch (*Perca fluviatilis*)*

Substance	Lethal concentration (p.p.m.) Sunfish	Perch
Acetone . .	14,250–15,050	
Acridine . .		0·7
Amylene . .	655–693	
Aniline . .	1,020–1,122	
Anthracene .	?	?
Benzene . .	35–37	
Benzoic acid .	550–570	
Catechol . .		20
o-cresol . .	55–65	10–20
m-cresol . .		10–20
p-cresol . .	80–90	10–20
Guaiacol . .		70–80
Isoquinoline .	65	100
Naphthalene .	4–5	20–40
Phenanthrene .	1–2	?
Phenol . .	70–75	9–20
Pyridine . .	1,477–1,576	1,000
Quinoline . .	52–56	30–50
Rosolic acid .		100
Thiophene .	27	
Toluene . .	61–65	
Xylene . .	47–48	

* For sunfish the concentrations are those fatal in 1 h at 20° C. For perch the concentrations are those in which the fish died in 1 h or died after transference to water after 1 h in the solution. The temperature of the perch experiments is not given in the data. A query indicates that the substance was tested but that there was no definite result. The data are taken from References 5 and 7.

Shelford reviews the results with all the substances tested individually. Most of them produced a condition that may be described as intoxication. The fish appeared to be stimulated at first—wild and erratic swimming with trembling of the fins might continue for some time—then they would lose their sense of balance, turn over and die, or go into a state resembling anaesthesia. Quinoline produced paralysis very quickly and a very deep anaesthesia, the fish living for some time after cessation of the breathing movements. Phenol and the cresols appeared to be highly irritating at first, later the fish became paralysed; naphthalene, on the other hand, produced no violent symptoms, the fish became intoxicated gradually and died without any erratic movement.

Many of these substances produce symptoms of intoxication in man; benzene and naphthalene are examples. In man aniline poisoning results from the conversion of haemoglobin to methaemoglobin by some compound formed from aniline in the blood, probably phenyl-hydroxylamine. Methaemoglobin is a bluish compound so that cyanosis is a characteristic feature of the condition. Early symptoms resemble inebriation; excitement, vertigo and mental confusion are followed by prostration, vomiting and a desire to sleep[6]. Phenol has an intense irritant action on mucous membranes, and in addition appears to have some direct disorganizing effect on the nervous system of higher animals. In frogs convulsions are produced as a result of increased irritability of the spinal cord, and later there is complete paralysis. In man there are tremors of the skeletal muscles, followed by convulsions and failure of the respiratory movements. Even small doses may produce nausea, vertigo and irregular respiration.

Shelford studied the reactions of fish to the gas waste and its various constituents with the gradient tank. In a few cases he found that a negative or avoiding action was displayed, but usually the reaction seen was of the type termed 'positive'; the fish swam into the waste or test solution and then tended to remain in it, avoiding the pure water. Shelford considered that his results showed that fish would tend to enter and remain in portions of streams contaminated by gas wastes and that this increased very much the seriousness of this type of pollution.

A long report dealing with the effects of pollution by tars used for road surfacing appeared in 1930[7]. This investigation was prompted by the deterioration, and in some cases the extinction, of fisheries adjacent to roads treated with tar. Perch were used as test fish and experiments were made with various extracts of tars and solutions of their various constituent compounds, including naphthalene, phenanthrene, anthracene, and tar bases, phenol and the cresols. For each substance the 'killing strength' was determined; at this concentration the fish either died in a 60 min exposure, or failed to survive on being transferred to water after an exposure of this time (Table 11). The symptoms observed were generally similar to those described by Shelford; the fish became intoxicated, and gulping and dashing movements were followed by loss of equilibrium. With phenol and the cresols the fish usually died with the mouth open and the gill covers raised. The gills were sometimes red, sometimes pale. In fish killed in quinoline the gills were congested and covered with mucus; the solution had a marked anaesthetic effect and some of the perch which were apparently dead recovered on transference to fresh water. Watery extracts made from a number of samples of tar were all fatal to perch within an hour. If tar bases (quinoline, pyridine and acridine) predominated in the sample, narcosis and paralysis were the characteristic symptoms. Extracts containing a high proportion of tar acids (phenols, cresols, guaiacol and catechol) produced irritation and dashing movements at first, followed by narcosis.

All the experiments so far discussed involved short exposure periods only, and the concentrations tested bear little relation to practical tolerance limits. Alexander, Southgate and Bassindale[8] in their study of pollution in the River Tees worked out survival curves for the rainbow trout, with phenol, p-cresol and 1-,2-,6-xylenol. The lethal limits for these three substances were about 6, 5 and 7 p.p.m. respectively. As in the studies previously discussed the very rapid effect of these substances on the equilibrium of the fish was noted, and the experiments were taken to confirm that they act as specific poisons on their nervous system. Wuhrmann and Woker[9] have reviewed the literature on the toxicity of phenol to fish and quote a number of limiting concentrations for various species, ranging from 0·5 p.p.m. to 20 p.p.m. Two of the values given are not correct; it is stated that according to Shelford a sunfish is killed in 1 h by 0·7 mg/l.; the correct figure is 70–75 p.p.m., and the concentration 0·4–0·6 mg/l. quoted from Alexander, Southgate and Bassindale should be 4–6 p.p.m. The paper by Wuhrmann and Woker is mainly a study of the relation between concentration and survival time. Four species of fish were studied: trout, perch, minnow and chub. The survival times plotted on logarithmic scales follow curves conforming to the equation $(C-a)^n(T-b)=K$ discussed in Chapter 4. For the trout, when the time is in minutes and the concentration is in mg/l. the equation of Wuhrmann and Woker is $(C-9)^{1\cdot128}(T-2)=70\cdot2$ and for the perch the equation is $(C-12)^{1\cdot202}(T-3)=344$.

Spent still liquor rarely contains any great concentration of cyanide and its chief toxic constituents are ammonia and monohydric phenols. A study of the combined action of ammonia and a mixture of monohydric phenols in the proportions in which they occur in spent still liquor has been carried out at the Water Pollution Research Laboratory. It is known that the toxicity of ammonia is very dependent on the pH (see Chapter 8). The monohydric phenols were found to have about the same degree of toxicity over the pH range 5·83–8·10, and the mixture was not toxic when the total amount present was below 4·4 p.p.m. and the solution contained no ammonia.   If it is assumed that the toxicity of ammonia and the monohydric phenols is additive, a mixture in which the concentration of ammonia is half the threshold, and that of the phenols is also half the threshold should have a threshold toxicity.   Extending this argument to cover all mixtures, if A_S and P_S are the concentrations of ammonia and phenols, and A_T and P_T are the thresholds, the mixture should have no

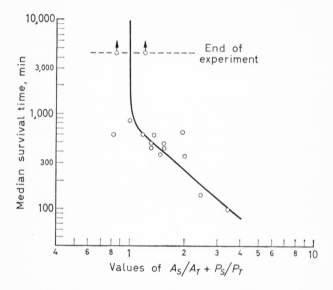

Figure 51.   Survival times of rainbow trout in solutions of ammonia and phenol plotted against values of $A_S/A_T + P_S/P_T$.   Temperature 10·2–11·3° C

appreciable toxicity when the value of $(A_S/A_T + P_S/P_T)$ does not exceed unity.   To test this hypothesis the survival times of trout were determined for a series of mixtures containing 0·17–0·66 p.p.m. of un-ionized ammonia and 1·9–10·0 p.p.m. of monohydric phenols.   In *Figure 51* the survival times are plotted against values of $(A_S/A_T + P_S/P_T)$ and it will be seen that the mixtures are non-toxic when this does not exceed 1.   The formula appears to predict the toxicity of ammonia–phenol mixtures with a useful degree of accuracy.   Care should be taken to use a threshold value for ammonia which is correct for the pH and free carbon dioxide content of the water; in *Figure 51* the value of A_T is 0·60.   The undiluted phenol mixture contained 53·6 per cent of phenol, 15·3 per cent of m-cresol, 12·9 per cent of p-cresol, and smaller quantities of o-cresol and various xylenols[10].

The threshold concentration value for the mixture of phenols is somewhat lower than that given for the trout by Wuhrmann and Woker (9 p.p.m.); this, however, is for pure phenol.   Leclerc and Devlaminck[11] find that phenol is toxic to minnows down to 24–28 p.p.m. in distilled water, and is slightly more toxic in hard water, the limit in this case being 18–20 p.p.m.   These values seem rather high but they are based on exposure times of only 6 h.   Limiting concentrations based on field observations are much lower than those obtained by experiment; thus according to Kalabina[12] fish are not generally found in waters containing more than 0·2 p.p.m. of phenol. Kalabina notes, however, that in such cases some other very toxic compounds such as naphthalene, resins and cyanides may be present.

The data available seem to show that the sensitivity to phenol of most fish is of much the same order.   Hubault[13] found that at 21° C a 20 p.p.m. solution is fatal to white roach and red roach in about 2 h. Härdtl[14] found the limiting concentration for perch to be about 20 p.p.m. and according to Trama[15] the 96 h TL_m for the bluegill is $19·3 \pm 2$ p.p.m.   A recent study of the toxicity of phenolic substances to carp, tench and roach is that of Albersmeyer and Erichsen[16]. They have shown that while phenol, the cresols and the xylenols all have a toxic action of generally similar type, their degree of toxicity varies considerably.   Thus in the experiments with carp it was found that 1-,3-,5-xylenol is by far the least toxic of the range tested.   At 18° C the minimum 'latent period', i.e. the time that passes before toxic symptoms are apparent, is 300 sec.   The other xylenols, the cresols and phenol have much shorter latent periods.   Median lethal doses were determined and these are given in Table 12.   Ten fish were used at each concentration tested, in 600 l. volumes of solution.

Albersmeyer and Erichsen have also shown that the different monohydric phenols vary somewhat in the speed with which they are taken up, and excreted, by carp.   1-,4-,5-xylenol seems to be absorbed most quickly and o-cresol the least quickly; the order is very different from the order of increasing toxicity.   When taken into the tissues of fish, phenolic substances are said to give them an unpleasant flavour.   According to Boetius[17] chlorophenol is particularly bad in this respect; an unpleasant flavour may be acquired from water containing only 0·0001 p.p.m. as the fish concentrate this substance in their fatty tissues.

Survival curves for minnows in solutions of phenol, o-cresol and p-cresol are given in *Figure 52*.   These curves were worked out as a

147

Table 12.   The Toxicity of Monohydric Phenols to Carp, Tench and Roach*

Substance	DL 50 (p.p.m.)		
	Carp	Tench	Roach
1-,4-,5-xylenol	10	9	10
o-cresol	29·5	15·4	15·6
p-cresol	21·2	15·8	17
1-,2-,4-xylenol	21·1	17·8	15·6
phenol	24·9	14·5	17
m-cresol	24·5	21	23·3
1-,3-,4-xylenol	30	13	no test
1-,3-,5-xylenol	53	51·5	no test

* The concentrations are 50 per cent lethal doses for exposure periods of 24 h at 18° C and 8 p.p.m. oxygen.   Data from Albersmeyer and Erichsen[16].

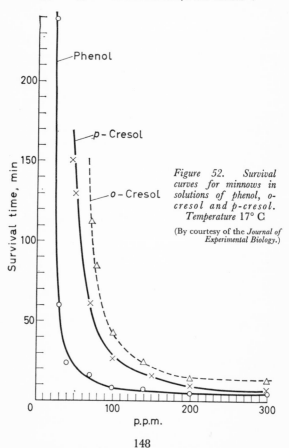

Figure 52.   Survival curves for minnows in solutions of phenol, o-cresol and p-cresol. Temperature 17° C

(By courtesy of the *Journal of Experimental Biology*.)

preliminary to experiments on the reactions of fish to phenolic substances[18], with the reaction-tube apparatus described in Chapter 3. It will be seen that phenol is the most toxic and *o*-cresol the least toxic of the three substances. The times are killing times; the overturning times for corresponding concentrations are very much shorter. In *p*-cresol solutions, for example, the overturning times are under 2 min for concentrations above 50 p.p.m. The behaviour of the fish in the solutions conformed well with the descriptions given by other workers. In the stronger solutions the sense of balance is lost almost at once. There are wild, dashing movements in which the fish may be on its side, or on its back. Later all attempts at swimming are very feeble

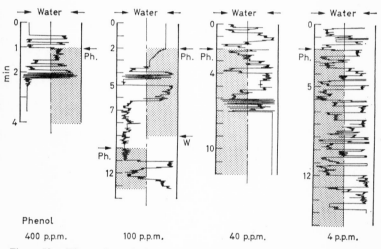

Figure 53. The reactions of minnows to phenol solutions. pH *of water* 6·8; pH *of solutions* 6·6–6·8. *Temperature* 16·5–17·5° C. *Survival times at these concentrations (in survival time experiments)* 4 min, 8 min, 24 min, 40–50 h

(By courtesy of the *Journal of Experimental Biology*.)

and the opercular movements are shallow and flickering. In the weaker solutions the sense of balance is affected rather more gradually; the fish falls over but may regain its equilibrium a number of times. Finally, however, it loses all power of co-ordinated movement and lies on its side with respiratory movements that are almost imperceptible. This helpless condition prevails for the rest of the survival time, the death-point being very ill-defined.

Four typical results obtained with phenol solutions when minnows were tested with the reaction tube are shown in *Figure 53*. In the 400 p.p.m. experiment the phenol was admitted on the right when the fish was in the left half of the apparatus; however, it entered the solution at once, where it gulped and moved very jerkily, visited the water zone and returned twice, at 2 min lost its sense of balance, swam wildly up and down the tube about six times, and finally stopped in the water where it began to recover. In the 100 p.p.m. experiment the solution was run in on the side occupied by the fish. For a short time it seemed unaffected but symptoms of intoxication developed very suddenly at about 4 min, with a fit of dashing. At 5–6 min the fish was in the solution, moving very feebly, and then it found its way into the water, where it recovered very quickly. At 8 min it was swimming upright and at 10 min the phenol was run in on the left, when the fish once more failed to recognize it and was again intoxicated. It recovered very quickly in the aquarium. At 40 p.p.m. the result is very similar, the symptoms of intoxication taking a little longer to develop. The fish persisted in swimming into the solution and lost its equilibrium at about 6 min. The fish also kept swimming into the solution at 4 p.p.m. but no symptoms of intoxication developed during the period of the test. The record of the fish's movements show that it hesitated at the water-solution junction about three times; the other crossings were made without any pause. In all, 12 experiments were carried out with phenol; in none did the fish show any capability of recognizing the solution.

Twelve experiments were run with *p*-cresol, covering the concentration range 300–20 p.p.m. Four records are shown in *Figure 54*; this includes two records for 300 p.p.m. to illustrate the good agreement observed in different tests. At 300 p.p.m., in marked contrast to what is seen with the higher concentrations of phenol, a most definite avoiding action was evident. The minnows would not enter the solution at all; on encountering it they would stop, back away or turn, usually gobbling or 'coughing'. At this concentration *p*-cresol is so toxic that these momentary contacts were sufficient to affect the fish somewhat and at the end of the experiment they were distressed, but still swimming upright. At 100 p.p.m. the solution appeared to be much less irritating and the fish did not seem to be able to detect it. The record shows that six or seven ventures into the right-hand side of the apparatus resulted in intoxication, but the fish settled in the water, recovered, and at 8 min was swimming quite normally. At 30 p.p.m. the minnows were excited by the solution but did not lose their equilibrium. A series of experiments with *o*-cresol gave very similar results. At 400 p.p.m. the fish appeared to be very irritated by the solution and avoided it with fair success, but at 200 p.p.m. and lower concentrations the reaction failed.

In addition to the foregoing experiments with pure solutions of phenol and cresol a number of trials were made with various dilutions of a phenolic effluent supplied by a firm of manufacturing chemists. The neat effluent was a clear, slightly tawny solution of pH 6·8 and strong 'carbolic' odour. The total concentration of phenolic substances, including phenol, cresols and xylenols was stated to be approximately 762 p.p.m.; other substances present were sodium sulphite, sodium chloride and sodium sulphate. A 1:10 dilution of this effluent, fatal in 35 min in a survival time experiment, did not appear to be recognized, the fish entering it with no hesitation, and 1:20, 1:40 and 1:100 dilutions similarly produced no negative response.

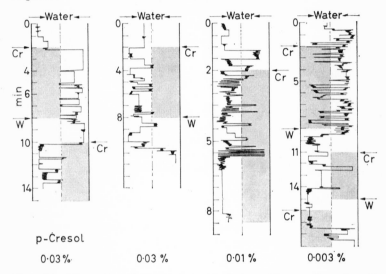

Figure 54. The reactions of minnows to p-cresol solutions. Two records are shown for 300 p.p.m. pH of water and solutions 6·8. Temperature 17·5–18° C

(By courtesy of the *Journal of Experimental Biology*.)

It has been shown that fish seem to be able to recognize and avoid dilute solutions of lead and zinc salts, and that they may establish this avoiding action in a time which is a small fraction of the survival time. These salts have no special disorganizing effect on the animal's nervous system and so the conditions are not critical. In the case of phenol there appears to be little chance of fish avoiding the solution at any concentration. With the cresols the conditions appear to be very critical, as the solution destroys their equilibrium so quickly.

151

REFERENCES

[1] *Water Pollution Research, 1956.* 1957. London; H.M.S.O.
[2] *Water Pollution Research, 1957.* 1958. London; H.M.S.O.
[3] Klein, L. *Aspects of River Pollution.* 1957. London; Butterworths
[4] Brown, A. W. A. *Insect Control by Chemicals.* 1951. London; John Wiley
[5] Shelford, V. E. An experimental study of the effects of gas wastes upon fishes, with especial reference to stream pollution. *Bull. Ill. Lab. nat. Hist.,* 11 (1917) 381–412
[6] Goodman, L. S. and Gilman, A. *The Pharmacological Basis of Therapeutics,* 2nd edn. 1955. New York; Macmillan
[7] Ministry of Transport, and Ministry of Agriculture and Fisheries. Detailed Biological and Chemical Reports on Tars used for Road-surfacing. 1930. London; H.M.S.O.
[8] Alexander, W. B., Southgate, B. A. and Bassindale, R. Survey of the River Tees. Pt. II. The estuary—chemical and biological. *Tech. Pap. Wat. Pollut. Res., Lond.,* No. 5 (1935)
[9] Wuhrmann, K. and Woker, H. Die Giftikeit von Phenol für verschiedene Fischarten. *Schweiz. Z. Hydrol.* 12 (1950) 271–87
[10] *Water Pollution Research, 1960.* 1961. London; H.M.S.O.
[11] Leclerc, E. and Devlaminck, F. Recherches du C.B.E.D.E. sur la toxicologie des poissons. *Bull. du C.B.E.D.E.,* No. 15 (1952) 66–7
[12] Kalabina, M. M. The decomposition of phenol in running and standing waters. *Z. Fisch.,* 33 (1935) 295. Cited from *Summ. curr. Lit. Wat. Pollut.,* 9 (1936) 215
[13] Hubault, E. The toxicity of various phenols towards fresh-water fish. *C.R. Acad. Agric. Fr.,* 22 (1936) 324. Cited from *Summ. curr. Lit. Wat. Pollut.,* 9 (1936) 431
[14] Härdtl, H. The toxicity to fish of the water-soluble constituents of different tar products with special reference to road tars and impregnated substances. *Z. Fisch.,* 32 (1934) 459. Cited from *Summ. curr. Lit. Wat. Pollut.,* 9 (1936) 179
[15] Trama, F. B. The acute toxicity of phenol to the common bluegill (*Lepomis macrochirus* Rafinesque). *Notul. nat. Acad. Philad.,* 269 (1955) 1–10
[16] Albersmeyer, W. and Erichsen, L. v. Untersuchungen zur Wirkung von Teerbestandteilen in Abwässern. *Z. Fisch.,* 8 N. F. (1959) 29–65
[17] Boetius, J. Foul taste of fish and oysters caused by chlorophenol. *Medd. Denmarks Fishl-og Havundersdg.* N.S. 1 (1954) 1–8
[18] Jones, J. R. E. The reactions of the minnow, *Phoxinus phoxinus* (L.) to solutions of phenol, ortho-cresol and para-cresol. *J. exp. Biol.,* 28 (1951) 261–70

13

THERMAL POLLUTION: THE EFFECT
OF HEATED EFFLUENTS

THE generation of electricity in thermal plant (steam turbines and diesel engines) involves the use of very large quantities of cooling water, which is drawn from and returned to rivers, estuaries and the sea. The cooling water effluent may be quite inoffensive chemically, but it may be sufficiently warm and in such quantity as to make a considerable change in the temperature of the watercourse into which it is discharged. This 'thermal pollution' is a potential hazard to fish and has attracted a good deal of attention recently. A number of different results may follow: the viscosity of the water will be changed slightly but there is no evidence to show that this effect is of any great importance; the rate at which the flowing water absorbs oxygen from the air will be increased[1], but the amount it can hold in solution will fall; if oxidizable material is present the rate at which this will remove oxygen from solution will be increased by a rise in the temperature; an excessive development of water weed or sewage fungus may be observed and there may be changes in the nature and density of the invertebrate fauna. A discussion of all these aspects of the problem is beyond the scope of this work and here the direct effect of thermal pollution on fish is examined.

In any river or stream in which a flow of water is maintained the continual mixing of the water prevents the establishment of a thermal stratification such as that found in lakes. Even in the largest rivers there are no significant differences between surface and bottom temperatures. The temperature of a river depends on a number of factors: the temperature of the air above and whether it is still or moving; the temperature of the soil mass below the bed, and the radiant energy of the sun. The last is very important in the case of clear and shallow waters, as the sun's rays heat up the bottom, which then warms the water above. Weedy and turbid rivers therefore tend to be cooler than clear rivers, and streams fed by springs also tend to be cold. Aspect is important also; in northern latitudes streams flowing down a hillside facing the south may be many degrees warmer than those flowing down north-facing slopes, the converse being found, of course, in southern latitudes. The size of the watercourse determines the rapidity with which the temperature varies in response to all these factors; in the smallest streams the temperature may change from hour to hour, in the largest rivers the changes may be almost entirely seasonal.

In cool but very sunny weather, in the spring or early summer, the water temperature of a clear, shallow, unshaded stream may exceed the air temperature by several degrees[2] due to the heating effect of the sun's rays on the bottom, but in the warm season of the year, in temperate latitudes, the maximum temperature of rivers of moderate or large size does not attain the same value as the air maximum, and is usually some 3–4° C lower. Thus Berg's records for the River Susaa in Denmark[3] include no values above 24·8° C and in the British Isles river temperatures above 25° C must be of very rare occurrence. American rivers may be much warmer and Murray[4] found many in northern Indiana whose temperature could exceed 28° C; in three cases the maximum was over 31° C. Huntsman[5] has noted the death of fish in Canadian streams in which the June temperature exceeded 31° C.

It is in the interests of efficient power generation to keep the amount of heat discharged in the cooling system to a minimum. The efficiency of the generating plant, its size and the amount of cooling water available are factors determining the temperature of the water discharged. Some old and inefficient plants, operating on a comparatively low steam pressure, dissipate in the cooling water system from 9,000 to as much as 12,000 B.Th.U. per unit of electricity generated. More modern plant is much more efficient and the exhaust heat may be only 5,300–5,500 B.Th.U. per unit, with high pressure steam cycles designed to operate under good vacuum conditions. Where there is a very large supply of cooling water available the system might be designed for a cooling water temperature rise of 5·6–6·7° C at full load; if the amount of water available is more limited, in order to effect the same amount of cooling a greater temperature rise must be accepted and the designed rise may be 7·8–8·3° C. A power station with an exhaust heat of 6,000 B.Th.U. per unit generated, designed for a temperature rise of 5·6° C, and working on the 'open' system in which the water is only used once, will require 60 gal. of water per unit generated, or 40 gal. if the temperature rise is 8·3° C. This means that the cooling water requirements of a 100,000 kW power station would be 4–6 million gallons of water per hour[6]. This would be the total discharge of a river 80 ft. wide, 0–4 ft. deep and with an average current velocity of about 1·4 ft./sec. A coal-fired 400 MW station would require a supply of water greater than the summer flow of the

Thames above Teddington and a nuclear station of the same capacity would require twice as much as a coal-fired station[7]. Less water is used if it is circulated through cooling towers and re-used, but cooling towers are expensive to construct and operate as power has to be expended in pumping the water through them. Furthermore their construction meets with much opposition from planning authorities and local residents.

Some studies have been made of the temperature changes of rivers into which cooling water is discharged. Records for the River Lee, a tributary of the Thames, show that in November and December 1956 the river might be warmed by 4–12° C immediately below the point of discharge and by 4–8° C or more two miles downstream. The variation in the heating effect, which is moderately regular and diurnal in periodicity, is presumably due to changes in the load on the power station[8]. A table of the physical and chemical properties of the water used for cooling at a number of British power stations is given in a recent paper by Markowski[9]; the maximum temperature of outlet water recorded in this table is 31·3° C, this is for the power station at Leicester on the River Soar.

The generation of electricity is not the only cause of thermal pollution. Some discharge of heated water may be associated with the cooling of gas at gas-works, and if the system known as direct cooling is used, in which the water comes into contact with the gas, the effluent may be chemically polluted as well as hot. The concentration of sulphuric acid in pot stills and the manufacture of sugar from sugar beet may result in the discharge of considerable volumes of hot condenser water. Other industrial processes associated with heated effluents are the preparation of dried milk, the pickling of steel and the washing of wool.

It has been known for some time that cold-blooded animals can become acclimatized to temperatures above or below those to which they are normally subjected, but the extent to which they can do this, and the means by which they achieve this acclimatization, after much study and speculation remains something of a mystery. By losing water vapour in expired air and in sweat, warm-blooded animals can survive air temperatures above their normal body temperatures provided that the humidity of the atmosphere is not too great. Such body temperature regulation is not possible in fish. Any temperature changes in the surrounding water are immediately communicated to the blood circulating in the gills and the blood passes them on to the whole of the animal's body. Heat insulation of the integument would therefore serve no purpose, and heat insulation of the gill membranes could not be effective without destroying their efficiency as respiratory

155

organs. The state of a fish placed in excessively warm water is very different from that of a man placed in excessively warm air. The man takes into his lungs a gas mixture of comparatively low heat capacity and containing a high proportion of oxygen; by sweating he can lose heat from the skin. The fish obviously cannot lose heat in this way and has to pass through its respiratory system a liquid of high heat capacity in considerable quantities on account of the relatively small amount of oxygen it contains. In excessively warm water, therefore, the body temperature of the fish must rise and the animal will be in danger of 'heat death'.

Heat death is a problem in animal physiology that has been extensively studied but is not satisfactorily explained. It has been attributed to the coagulation of cell proteins and to the inactivation of enzymes, and the possibility that the resistance of animals to high temperatures may depend upon the melting points of the fats in their bodies has been extensively studied. Experiments with the skate and the flounder have shown that heat death seems to result from failure of the co-ordinating mechanisms of the central nervous system; as the temperature is raised various reflexes disappear in a consistent sequence[10]. The whole subject has been reviewed by Heilbrunn[11].

It is customary, now, to use the term acclimatization for a change in tolerance to heat or cold that comes about slowly, under natural conditions, and to use the term 'acclimation' to refer to a change in tolerance that is induced experimentally and more or less quickly. One of the earliest papers dealing with the adaptation of fish to high temperatures is that of Loeb and Wasteneys[12], who showed that the mud-minnow, *Fundulus*, dies in about 4 min in distilled water at 35° C, but fish that have been kept for 30 h or more at a temperature of 27° C are more or less immunized to 35° C. The immunity, when acquired, is not easily lost or weakened by subsequent exposure to lower temperatures. Exposure to 10–14° C for 33 days resulted in no loss of heat tolerance and the immunity to 35° C is retained even after two weeks at 0·4° C. The acclimation need not be effected by a long, continuous exposure to a high temperature. A similar result can be brought about by intermittent exposure to a high temperature for a number of hours each day.

Hathaway[13] carried out a more extensive study of the heat tolerance of fish and determined the maximum temperatures at which four species could survive for 24 h. These were: yellow perch, 29·6° C; largemouth bass, 32·2° C; bluegill, 34° C and sunfish (*Eupomotus gibbosus*), 34° C. He found that within each species individuals of different ages appeared to have about the same temperature limits, and that a change in the temperature survived could be brought about by acclimation. Hathaway has an interesting method of computing his results; the value expressing the heat tolerance (T) of the species tested is given by the formula:

$$T = \frac{tP_1 + (t-2)P_2 + (t-4)P_3}{100}$$

where t is the highest temperature survived for the given period by *any* of the individuals tested; $t-2$ and $t-4$ are temperatures 2 and 4 degrees below t, and P_1, P_2 and P_3 are the percentages of individuals surviving these temperatures. For largemouth bass t is 34° C; P_1, P_2 and P_3 are 26, 60 and 14 so that T works out to 32·24° C.

Sumner and Wells[14] noted that tolerance to high temperatures, once acquired, may persist for considerable periods after the return of the organism to the temperature from which it was taken, or even to a considerably lower one. Wells[15], experimenting with mud suckers (*Gillichthys mirabilis*) showed that fish acclimated to high temperatures have a much lower rate of metabolism at a common intermediate temperature than fish acclimated to a low temperature. The first complete study of thermal tolerance and acclimation in a fish is that of Fry, Brett and Clawson[16]. This was followed by further studies by Fry, Hart and Walker[17] and Hart[18]. Their conclusions may be summarized as follows:

For any particular acclimation temperature every species of fish has a temperature range within which 'existence' for an indefinite period is possible. This range has an upper limit, the 'thermal death-point' or 'upper incipient lethal temperature', above which the animal cannot live indefinitely but survives for some limited period. Similarly there is a 'cold death-point', or 'lower incipient lethal temperature'; usually this is freezing point but in the case of fish acclimated to high temperatures it may be a number of degrees above freezing. Between the thermal death-point and the cold death-point we have the condition termed 'tolerance'; at temperatures above the upper limit and below the lower limit the animal is said to be in a condition of 'resistance'. Above the thermal death-point the resistance time shortens with a progressive rise in temperature until a point is reached at which the animal is killed instantaneously on transference from water at the acclimation temperature.

If the acclimation temperature is raised the thermal death-point usually rises also, and at high acclimation temperatures the lower limit may be moved up, sometimes to several degrees above freezing. The rise in the thermal death-point is less than the rise in the acclimation temperature; thus in the roach, raising the acclimation temperature 3° C raises the thermal death-point about 1° C[19, 20]. Accordingly, for every species of fish a stage is reached where the acclimation temperature catches up on the thermal death-point, and so an 'ultimate upper lethal temperature' is reached. This limit to acclimation also sets a limit to changes in the lower incipient lethal temperature, and so the complete thermal reaction graph for the fish comes to be represented by a figure of the type shown in *Figure 55*, a figure which is 4-, 5-, or 6-sided, but which, in the literature, is usually, though sometimes inaccurately, called a trapezium or trapezoid. Within the trapezium we have a 'zone of tolerance', including all the temperatures at which indefinite existence is possible; to the right are temperatures at which acclimation is not possible; above the trapezium is a

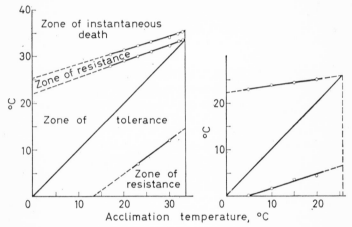

Figure 55. *The thermal relations of the roach (left) and the coho salmon (right)*
(Drawn from the data of Cocking[19] and Brett[22].)

'zone of resistance'—temperatures the fish can endure for a limited period—and a 'zone of instantaneous death'. Below the trapezium is another zone of resistance—to cold. Fry, Brett and Clawson[16] consider that the slope of the resistance to cold line indicates that the thermal tolerance may pass outside the range of liquid water, and that when the acclimation temperature is low the fish should survive temperatures below zero.

The figure expressing the thermal tolerance assumes complete acclimation. This is a process which may proceed at different speeds in different species and which may be much slower at descending than at ascending temperatures. Loss of resistance to high temperatures when colder conditions are experienced may take many days, but adaptation to high temperatures may take place in a matter of hours.

Thus Brett[21] found that fathead minnows took over 20 days to become completely acclimated to 16° C after previously living at 24° C, but became acclimated to 28° C from 20° C in 24 h. Brett has also shown that changes in the thermal tolerance of fish take place under natural conditions; thus in Lake Opeongo, Ontario, the lethal temperatures of the fish show seasonal changes of several degrees, in keeping with the changes in the temperature of the lake. Brett's records for the catfish, *Ameiurus nebulosus*, are set out in *Figure 56*.

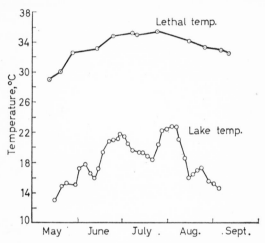

Figure 56. *Seasonal variation in the lethal temperature of the catfish* (Ameiurus nebulosus) *taken from Lake Opeongo, Ontario, and the variation in the average temperature of the lake water, May–September 1941*

(Drawn from the data of Brett[21].)

The size of the trapezium depicting the range of temperatures a fish can survive is an indication of its general degree of thermal tolerance. Working out the area of the trapezium in 'square degrees' can give us a numerical value for the thermal tolerance. Values for a number of species have been computed and are given in a table in the review by Brett[22]. The chum salmon has the very low thermal tolerance of 468 square degrees, associated with its normal habitat of cool streams; at the other extreme are the catfish, *Ameiurus nebulosus*, and the goldfish, with scores of 1,162 and 1,220. These are types adapted for life in very shallow and warm water. The common sucker (770) and the fathead minnow (903) are species of an intermediate grade of thermal tolerance.

Brett's figures[22] are for American fish. Much greater attention has been paid to American species than to those of Britain and Europe, probably because American rivers tend to be warmer and more attention has to be paid to temperature limits when stocking is under consideration[23]. Recently more attention has been given to British species and Cocking[19, 20] has made a detailed study of the thermal tolerance of the roach. Some figures are available for the brown trout and the Atlantic salmon.

Thermal death-points for a number of British, European and American fish are given in Table 13. In selected cases the changes in thermal death-point brought about by moving the acclimation temperature are indicated, and it will be seen that different species react to very different extents in this respect. For example, when the acclimation temperature is raised from 10 to 30° C the thermal death-point of the fathead minnow goes up 5°; raising the acclimation temperature from 5 to 25° C results in the thermal death-point of the speckled trout being elevated only 1·6° C.

Table 13. Thermal Death-points of Fish

Fish	Acclimation temp. (°C)	Thermal death-point (°C)	Ref.
Bluegill	15	30·7	22
Brook stickleback . .	25–26	30·6	21
Brown trout . .	26	26	22
,, ,, (fry) . .	5–6	22·5	32
,, ,, ,, .	20	23	32
,, ,, (yearling) . .	?	25·91	33
,, ,, ('parr') .	?	29	33
Carp	20	31–34	35
Catfish or brown bullhead .	15	31·8	21
Chinook salmon (fry) . .	15	25	22
,, ,, ,, .	20	25·1	22
Chum salmon (fry) . .	15	23·1	22
,, ,, ,, .	20	23·7	22
Coho salmon (fry) . .	15	24·3	22
,, ,, ,, .	20	25	22
Common shiner . .	15	30·3	18
Common sucker . . .	15	29·3	18
Creek chub . . .	15	29·3	22
Fathead minnow . . .	10	28·2	18
,, ,, . .	20	31·7	18
,, ,, . .	30	33·2	18
Golden shiner . . .	15	30·5	22
Goldfish	10	30·8	16
,, . . .	20	34·8	16
,, . . .	30	38·6	16
Guppy	30	34	36
Largemouth bass . .	20	32·5	22

Table 13—cont.

Fish	Acclimation temp. (°C)	Thermal death-point (°C)	Ref.
Largemouth bass . .	30	36·4	22
Perch . . .	?	23–25	11
Pink salmon (fry) . .	5	21·3	22
,, ,, ,, . .	10	22·5	22
,, ,, ,, . .	20	23·9	22
Pumpkinseed . . .	25–26	34·5	21
Rainbow trout . . .	?	28	4
,, ,, (Kamloops var.)	11	24	35
Roach	20	29·5	19
,, ...	25	30·5	19
,, ...	30	31·5	19
Salmon (Salmo salar)			
grilse	?	29·5–30·5	37
parr	?	32·5–33·8	37
,, ...	?	29·8	33
Sockeye salmon (fry) . .	5	22·2	22
,, ,, ,, . .	10	23·4	22
,, ,, ,, . .	20	24·8	22
Speckled trout . . .	5	23·7	17
,, ,, . . .	10	24·4	17
,, ,, . . .	15	25	17
,, ,, . . .	20	25·3	17
,, ,, . . .	25	25·3	17
Tench	?	29–30	34
Yellow perch . . .	15	27·7	18

The possible effects of thermal pollution on fish from three points of view may now be examined. In the first place, how far can the temperature rises produced by hot effluents harm them by diminishing the solubility of oxygen? Secondly, how great is the danger of heat death? Thirdly, when the elevation of temperature is not so great as to be fatal, what adverse effects may it have upon the physiology of the fish affected? The way in which the solubility of oxygen decreases with rise in temperature is discussed in Chapter 2; provided that the river water and the cooling water discharged are reasonably pure, thermal pollution is not likely to be fatal to fish as a result of changes in the oxygen supply. Removing oxygen from water by warming it is a comparatively slow process; if the temperature rise is moderate the only result may be the setting up of some degree of supersaturation, and on cooling the water may still have its original supply[7]. Even at 30° C it can hold 7·53 p.p.m. of oxygen, which is well above the minimum requirement of the most sensitive fish, though it may not be sufficient for full activity. During the day a high water temperature may be accompanied by very active photosynthesis by the plants, so that the water may become super-saturated. Unfortunately there appear to be few cases in which heated water is discharged into unpolluted streams; in most cases it is discharged into water which is already polluted, and if the polluting matter is oxidizable its effects may be considerably aggravated.

A consideration of the figures in Table 13 leads to the conclusion that while certain species can withstand water temperatures that are decidedly high, others, such as the trout and the Pacific salmon, have

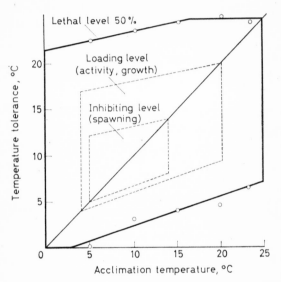

Figure 57.   Upper and lower lethal temperatures for young sockeye salmon, the thermal zone outside which growth is poor, and the zone outside which temperature is likely to inhibit normal reproduction

(After Brett[24], by courtesy of the Robert A. Taft Engineering Center, Ohio.)

little chance of surviving any serious degree of thermal pollution. In the warm season of the year, when river temperatures may rise to 22–24° C under natural conditions, a further rise of 1° or 2° may be sufficient to result in heat death. Furthermore it must be emphasized that death-point temperatures determined experimentally represent the extreme limits of existence, and the temperature zone within which the life of the fish, in every way, can be said to be normal, may be very much more limited. Brett[24] has recently published a most interesting thermal tolerance graph for the sockeye salmon (*Figure 57*). This shows a large trapezium enclosing the temperatures of mere existence;

within this is a smaller trapezium showing the limits for adequate activity and growth, and within this is a still smaller trapezium defining the zone outside which normal reproduction is likely to be inhibited. Evidence is accumulating to show that temperatures which are not so high as to cause death may have very adverse effects on the life of fish. The activity of cold-blooded animals usually increases with a rise in the temperature, but the relation is complicated; it has been shown that in certain fish maximum activity is displayed at comparatively low temperatures, and that at higher temperatures it declines. Thus Gibson and Fry[25] have shown that whereas lake trout (*Salvelinus namaycush*) have an ultimate lethal

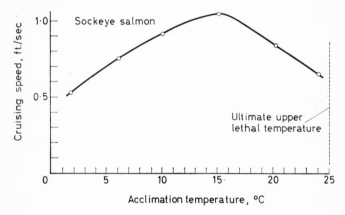

Figure 58.   Variation in cruising speed for temperature-acclimated underyearling sockeye salmon

(After Brett[24], by courtesy of the *Journal of the Fisheries Research Board of Canada*.)

temperature of 23·5° C their maximum maintained swimming speed is displayed at 16° C. Similarly the goldfish has a cruising speed which rises with the temperature up to about 28° C and then drops sharply, though acclimation to 41° C is possible[26]. *Figure 58* shows the effect of temperature on the cruising speed of young sockeye salmon, where the maximum occurs at about 15° C. The cruising speeds at 10° C and 19° C are approximately equal, but measurements of the oxygen consumption show that at 19° C the metabolic demand is much higher, so that for the same performance, at 19° C the energy reserves are exhausted $1\frac{1}{2}$–2 times as fast as at 10° C. It is shown in Chapter 2 that the difference between the resting oxygen consumption and the maximum possible at the prevailing temperature is a measure of the energy available for movement, feeding and the other essential functions of life—the 'scope for activity'. In many cases it is found that the standard, or resting, oxygen consumption rises more and more steeply as the temperature goes up, while the active oxygen consumption reaches a peak and then falls, so that the scope, the difference between the values, may become very restricted as the thermal death-point is approached (*Figure 59*). Measurements of swimming speeds and of the oxygen consumption of fish are made with the rotating respiration chamber described in Chapter 2. The results of these experiments and the conclusions drawn from them have been reviewed by Fisher[10].

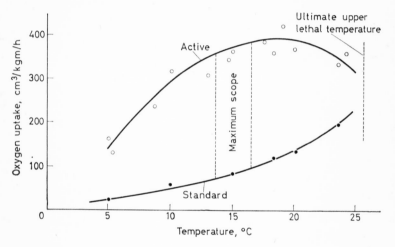

Figure 59.   The relation between oxygen uptake and temperature in acclimated speckled trout

(After Brett [24], by courtesy of the Robert A. Taft Sanitary Engineering Center, Ohio.)

A striking instance of the restrictive effects of high temperatures on the activity of trout was noted by Baldwin[27]; in experiments on food consumption in *Salvelinus fontinalis* (the speckled trout), in which live minnows were used as food, it was found that the trout were comparatively slow at catching the minnows at 17° C and virtually incapable of doing so at 21° C. Fisher and Elson[28] also found that the speckled trout displays most activity at comparatively low temperatures. They showed that the fish responds to an electrical stimulus by making a dart forwards; for the same stimulus the response, measured by the distance travelled, reaches a maximum at 10° C and this is the temperature selected by the fish when they are free to move in a temperature gradient. It has been found that brown trout grow more rapidly in cool water. Wingfield[29] discovered that an average daily temperature of 14·3° C gave the highest growth rate. Brown[30] found that there are two temperature ranges giving rapid growth: 7–9° C and 16–19° C.

It is probable that further research will show that for most fish the temperature zone within which the animal lives in complete comfort and success occupies a comparatively small trapezium inside that indicating the extreme limits of thermal tolerance. Brett[24] has proposed 'that the upper limit of required temperature for any species of

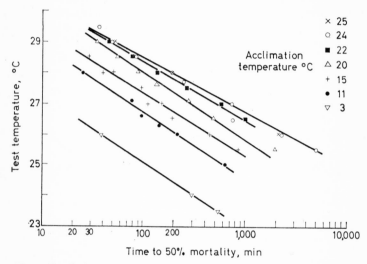

Figure 60. *Resistance times for speckled trout at various temperatures in the lethal range and for various levels of thermal acclimation*
(Drawn from the data of Fry, Hart and Walker[17].)

fish should not exceed that which would curtail activity below three-quarters of the optimum'. This suggested standard applies to waters normally at a temperature near the optimum. In the case of very cold waters thermal pollution may permit greatly increased activity, but acclimation to higher temperatures may make the fish more liable to cold death when the supply of warm water is interrupted. It is said that goldfish which live in the condenser ponds of a power station at Nottingham invariably die if transferred to water at normal temperature[6].

In cases where thermal pollution may produce a considerable but temporary rise of temperature the important question may be the time for which the fish can survive the conditions. The most complete study of 'resistance times' is that of Fry, Hart and Walker [17] with the speckled trout. Resistance times were determined for acclimation temperatures of 3–25° C (*Figure 60*). The relation between exposure temperature and time to 50 per cent mortality, plotted on a logarithmic scale, is linear. The slope of the graphs is much the same for all levels of acclimation and is such that a temperature rise of 2–2·5° C shortens the resistance time to about one-tenth its previous value.

Whether fish are killed in significant numbers by thermal pollution is doubtful, but they may disappear from heated regions of rivers, at least during the warm months of the year. Trembley [31] in a four-year study of the Delaware River above and below a generating plant found that there was an almost complete elimination of most species from the most heated zone during the warm months, but a congregation and extended period of feeding activity occurred in the heated water during the cold season of the year.

REFERENCES

[1] Truesdale, G. A. and Vandyke, K. G. The effect of temperature on the aeration of flowing water. *Water Waste Treatm. J.*, 7 (1958) 9–11

[2] Jones, J. R. E. An ecological study of the river Rheidol, north Cardiganshire, Wales. *J. Anim. Ecol.*, 18 (1949) 67–88

[3] Berg, K. Physiographical studies on the river Susaa. *Folia limnol. scand.*, No. 1 (1943) 174 pp.

[4] Murray, M. J. Survey of some northern Indiana streams with special reference to trout production. *Invest. Ind. Lakes*, 1 (1928–38) 79–99

[5] Huntsman, A. G. Heat stroke in Canadian maritime stream fishes. *J. Fish. Res. Bd Can.*, 6 (1946) 476–82

[6] Ministry of Housing and Local Government. *Prevention of River Pollution.* Report of the Rivers Pollution Prevention Sub-Committee of the Central Advisory Water Committee, Appendix C, 69–76, 1949, 1959. London; H.M.S.O.

[7] Ross, F. F. The operation of thermal power stations in relation to streams. *J. Inst. Sew. Purif.*, No. 1 (1959) 16–26

[8] *Water Pollution Research, 1958.* 1959. London; H.M.S.O.

[9] Markowski, S. The cooling water of power stations: a new factor in the environment of marine and freshwater invertebrates. *J. Anim. Ecol.* 28 (1959) 243–58

[10] Fisher, K. C. An approach to the organ and cellular physiology of adaptation to temperature in fish and small mammals. In *Physiological Adaptation*, ed. by C. L. Prosser. 1958. Washington; American Physiological Society, Inc.

[11] Heilbrunn, L. V. *An Outline of General Physiology*, 3rd edn. 1955. Philadelphia and London; Saunders

[12] Loeb, J. and Wasteneys, H. On the adaptation of fish (*Fundulus*) to higher temperatures. *J. exp. Zool.*, 12 (1912) 543–57

[13] Hathaway, E. S. Quantitative study of the changes produced by acclimatization in the tolerance of high temperatures by fish and amphibians. *Bull. U.S. Bur. Fish.*, 43 (1927) 169–92

[14] Sumner, F. B. and Wells, N. A. Some relations between respiratory metabolism in fishes and susceptibility to certain anaesthetics and lethal agents. *Biol. Bull., Wood's Hole*, 69 (1935) 368–78

[15] Wells, N. A. Change in rate of respiratory metabolism in a teleost fish induced by acclimatization to high and low temperature. *Biol. Bull., Wood's Hole*, 69 (1935) 361–7

[16] Fry, F. E. J., Brett, J. R. and Clawson, G. H. Lethal limits of temperature for young goldfish. *Rev. Canad. Biol.*, 1 (1942) 50–56

[17] Fry, F. E. J., Hart, J. S. and Walker, K. F. Lethal temperature relations for a sample of young speckled trout, *Salvelinus fontinalis*. *Univ. Toronto Stud. biol.*, 54 (1946) 35 pp.

[18] Hart, J. S. Lethal temperature relations of certain fish of the Toronto region. *Trans. roy. Soc. Can.*, 3rd Ser., Sect. V, 41 (1947) 57–71

[19] Cocking, A. W. The effects of high temperatures on roach (*Rutilus rutilus*). I. The effects of constant high temperatures. *J. exp. Biol.*, 36 (1959) 203–16.

[20] Cocking, A. W. The effects of high temperatures on roach (*Rutilus rutilus*). II. The effects of temperature increasing at a known constant rate. *J. exp. Biol.*, 36 (1959) 217–26

[21] Brett, J. R. Some lethal temperature relations of Algonquin Park fishes. *Univ. Toronto Stud. biol.*, 52 (1944) 49 pp.

[22] Brett, J. R. Some principles in the thermal requirements of fishes. *Quart. Rev. Biol.*, 31 (1956) 75–87

[23] James, M. C., Meehean, O. L. and Douglass, E. J. Fish stocking as related to the management of inland waters. *U.S. Fish Wildlife Serv. Conservation Bull.*, 35 (1944) 22 pp.

[24] Brett, J. R. Thermal requirements of fish—three decades of study, 1940–1970. In *Biological Problems in Water Pollution, Trans. 1959 Seminar Robert A. Taft Sanit. Eng. Cent. Tech. Rep. W60-3*, Cincinnati (1960)

[25] Gibson, E. S. and Fry, F. E. J. The performance of the lake trout, *Salvelinus namaycush*, at various levels of temperature and oxygen pressure. *Canad. J. Zool.*, 32 (1954) 252–60

[26] Fry, F. E. J. and Hart, J. S. Cruising speed of goldfish in relation to water temperature. *J. Fish. Res. Bd Can.*, 7 (1948) 169–75

[27] Baldwin, N. S. Food consumption and growth of brook trout at different temperatures. *Trans. Amer. Fish. Soc.*, 86 (1957) 323–8

[28] Fisher, K. C. and Elson, P. F. The selected temperature of Atlantic salmon and speckled trout and the effect of temperature on the response to an electrical stimulus. *Physiol. Zool.*, 23 (1950) 27–34

[29] Wingfield, C. A. The effect of certain environmental factors on the growth of brown trout (*Salmo trutta* L.). *J. exp. Biol.*, 18 (1940) 435–48

[30] Brown, M. E. The growth of brown trout (*Salmo trutta* Linn.). III. The effect of temperature on the growth of two-year-old trout. *J. exp. Biol.*, 22 (1946) 145–55

[31] Trembley, F. J. Research project on effects of condenser discharge water on aquatic life. Progress Report, 1956–1959. Institute of Research, Lehigh University, 1960. 154 pp

[32] Bishai, H. M.   Upper lethal temperatures for larval salmonids.   *J. Cons. int. Explor. Mer*, 25 (1960) 129–33

[33] Spaas, J. T.   Contribution to the comparative physiology and genetics of the European salmonidae.   III.   Temperature resistance at different ages.   *Hydrobiologia*, 15 (1960) 78–88

[34] Weatherley, A. H.   Some features of the biology of the tench *Tinca tinca* (Linnaeus) in Tasmania.   *J. Anim. Ecol.*, 28 (1959) 73–87

[35] Black, E. C.   Upper lethal temperatures of some British Columbia freshwater fishes.   *J. Fish. Res. Bd Can.*, 10 (1953) 196–210

[36] Gibson, M. B.   Upper lethal temperature relations of the guppy *Lebistes reticulatus*.   *Canad. J. Zool.*, 32 (1954) 393–407

[37] Huntsman, A. G.   Death of salmon and trout with high temperature.   *J. Fish. Res. Bd Can.*, 5 (1942) 485–501

14

SUSPENDED MATTER

THE suspended matter carried by rivers varies much in nature and particle size. Heavy and coarse particles can be carried only by very swift currents; very small particles, down to 10^{-4}mm in size are slow to settle and may give slow streams a temporary or persistent turbidity. Mineral suspended matter may come in wastes from sand washing, china-clay works and stone quarrying. Insoluble materials including chalk, talc, kaolin, gypsum and barium sulphate occur in paper-making wastes. Storm water sewage may contain 1,000–2,000 p.p.m. of suspended matter and this may have to be discharged to a receiving stream without being subjected to sedimentation or any other treatment. Organic particles in sewage effluents can bring about de-oxygenation of the water; gritty material carried by swift currents can scour away algal growth from the stream bed; excessive turbidity can cut off the light, reduce the photosynthesis of the submerged vegetation, and make it more difficult for the fish to find their food; heavy deposits of silt can foul the gravel of spawning beds and may be harmful to the invertebrate bottom fauna. In this chapter attention is concentrated on the possibility of direct injury to fish by suspended matter.

The gills of fish are delicate structures which could suffer mechanical injury by gritty particles, and there is also the danger of the gill system being clogged by an excessive amount of suspended matter. Crabs have long, feathery mastigobranchs, or gill cleaners, for removing foreign matter, but fish have no structures like these and have to rely on the flow of water through the gill chambers, the production of lubricating mucous secretions and intermittent, violent expulsion of water through the mouth or 'coughing'. Before the 'coagulation film anoxia' theory was advanced to explain the death of fish in rivers polluted by wastes from lead mines, it was widely believed that mechanical injury by grit was responsible, and all attempts to reduce the effects of pollution centred on sedimentation of the washing water.

It appears to be generally accepted that coal washing is not directly harmful to fish and that their absence from rivers polluted with coal dust is due to an absence of food. The suspended coal dust cuts off the light from the stream-bed, making the photosynthesis of plants impossible. Without plants there can be no invertebrates, and without plants and invertebrates there can be no fish. Some evidence to the contrary has been given; thus Pautzke[1], who studied the effect of coal washing on cutthroat and steelhead trout found that the fish died in $1\frac{1}{2}$–$2\frac{1}{2}$ h when placed in 'fish boats' in the polluted streams. The dead fish showed a heavy coating of mucus covering the body and gills and the colour of the gills had faded. It should be noted, however, that the coal mined above the site of the experiments was semibituminous in character, and that the washings contained slate and sand particles in considerable quantity. Pautzke's paper was published in 1937; recent work on the effect of coal-dust suspensions is described later in this chapter.

The earliest experimental work on the effects of suspended matter on fish appears to be that of Cole[2], who worked with wood fibres. He found that even a 2 per cent suspension was not harmful to healthy fish; after 3 weeks' treatment no damage to the gills was detected. Griffin[3] placed salmon and trout fingerlings in tanks of water containing up to 6,500 p.p.m. of silt. The water was stirred by hand from time to time and the fish survived 3–4 weeks.

Larsen and Olsen[4] have discussed the connection between the death of fish at a trout farm in West Jutland and the discharge of acid, iron-polluted water from lignite pits. The dead fish showed accumulations of ochre on the gills and it was concluded that this deposit of ochre proved fatal by preventing the diffusion of oxygen from the water to the gill blood vessels. It is possible, however, that the very high acidity of the iron-polluted water may have been partly responsible for the effects; some samples taken from the lignite pit had pH values of 3·0–3·4, and the pH of the stream below the drain from the pit varied from 3·4 to 5·4. At the trout farm, however, the pH readings were 6·0–7·0. One experiment is described in which some trout fingerlings were placed in an iron basket in the stream below the outflow from the lignite pit. When the experiment began the water was somewhat turbid but it soon became clear. In 6 h the fish, which had earlier shown some respiratory distress, were dead, with the slime of their bodies coagulated. There was a 'distinct accumulation' of ochre on their gills. The pH of the stream water was 4·35. As far as is known this degree of acidity is not lethal to trout, in the absence of other adverse factors.

Paul[5] has reported damage to fish in California by quartz grit. Wallen[6] in an experimental study of the effects of erosion silt on North American fish found that they lived over a week in 100,000 p.p.m. suspensions. Higher concentrations of the silt, 175,000–225,000 p.p.m., were fatal. The opercular cavities and the gill filaments of the fish that died were clogged with the clay particles, but macroscopic and microscopic examination of the gills gave no evidence of actual physical injury. Bartsch[7], discussing Wallen's results, points out that turbidities in the 'Big Muddy' Missouri from Williston to Yankton rarely exceed 7,000 p.p.m., and so it seems unlikely that natural turbidities will be directly lethal.

Stuart[8] in a study of the reproduction and young stages of trout, published in 1953, has examined the effects of silt on trout alevins. Newly hatched alevins were placed in flat trays and dishes which contained water charged with sediments, both natural and artificial. The natural sediments ranged from sand to very fine materials which remained in suspension for several hours. For up to 24 h after hatching the mouths of the alevins remained closed, and each, by movements of its pectoral fins, kept a space clear of sediment around its whole body. About 24 h after hatching their mouths opened and their gills began to function. Suspended matter stirred up by the movement of the alevins, now started to enter the gill chambers. Here, however, mucus-like secretion bound the particles together in a ropy formation and these strings were passed out, either through the gill openings or forward by coughing. In this way the alevins appeared to be able to cope with a certain amount of sediment, for the strings of mucus-bound particles, being comparatively heavy and bulky, were no longer stirred up by the water currents. Provided that the amount of sediment added did not exceed a layer about 1 mm deep on the bottom of the dish all the alevins survived. The continuous addition of suspended particles, however, built up to a situation that the alevins could not cope with; serious inflammation of the gill membranes was caused and this resulted in death. From his experiments Stuart concluded that a continuous influx of suspended matter from quarries, gravel pits and mines may be very detrimental to the young stages of trout; his statement that all the alevins survived when the sediment did not exceed a 1 mm layer is his only estimate of the threshold of tolerance.

A new study of the effect of mineral suspended matter on the survival of trout is that of Herbert and Merkens[9]. They point out that previous experimental work has shown that fish can survive extremely high concentrations of suspended matter for short periods; that a number of industrial processes involve the discharge of wastes which maintain appreciable concentrations of suspended solids in streams more or less indefinitely; and that tests for possible harm to fish must be carried out for long periods. Two types of apparatus were used in the experiments and both are shown in *Figure 61*. In type (*a*) the

171

upper part of the test vessel is cylindrical; its base is conical and from the bottom the suspension is continually drawn off by an airlift and conveyed to the top. Here the air is discharged while water and suspended matter return to the tank, and the return pipe is directed tangentially so that a swirling motion of the water is set up, helping to keep the particles in suspension. Near the bottom a screen prevents the fish from fouling the drain opening. This type of apparatus was not completely satisfactory for prolonged experiments; the fish tended to keep swimming around and contact with its walls and the bottom screen resulted in many of them developing sores. Type (*b*) proved more satisfactory. The glass aquarium carries a 3 in. plastic

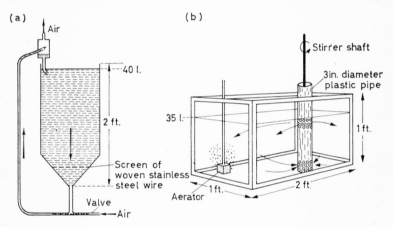

Figure 61. Aquaria for the study of the effect of suspended solids on fish
(From Herbert and Merkens[9], by permission of the Controller of H.M. Stationery Office, Crown copyright reserved.)

pipe, with two series of holes, one at the base and the other just below the water line. Inside the pipe a stainless steel propeller draws in the suspension and discharges it near the surface. The rate of circulation is about 35 l./min.

Ten rainbow trout 9–18 months old were used for each experiment and the solids used to make the suspensions were graded kaolin and diatomaceous earth. One series of tests was made with the apparatus with the conical base, this lasted 69 days; all the others were made with the rectangular aquaria and observations were continued for up to 185 days. All the fish were fed each day; after feeding they were removed to clean water while the apparatus was dismantled, cleaned and replenished, the fish then being returned. All the fish that died were examined to see whether they had wounds or signs of disease.

No significant mortality was noted at 30 p.p.m.; at 90 p.p.m. there was a small number of deaths. At 270 and 810 p.p.m. a high percentage of the fish died in the kaolin and diatomaceous earth suspensions, the latter appearing to be rather more harmful. In one experiment with 810 p.p.m. diatomaceous earth nearly 80 per cent of the fish were dead in about 14 days. The mortality among controls was negligible.

The gills of some of the fish to which the suspensions proved fatal were removed as soon as possible after death and prepared for histological examination. Comparison with preparations made from normal gills showed that there appeared to be a thickening of the cells of the respiratory epithelium, and in places adjacent lamellae were fused. The gills of some of the fish that survived the experiments were also examined; in some cases similar damage was evident but in others the condition of the respiratory epithelium was normal. A further experiment was now started with a 270 p.p.m. suspension of diatomaceous earth and fish were removed at intervals and killed so that their gills could be examined. After 148 days half the fish were taken out and transferred to 1,000 p.p.m. for the remainder of the experiment which continued for nearly 9 months. The results were rather inconclusive; in some cases thickening and fusion of the gill lamellae was seen again but some fish had perfectly normal gills after 8 months' contact with the suspensions. In a discussion of their results Herbert and Merkens conclude that there is no definite relation between the period of survival of fish exposed to high concentrations of suspended matter and the concentration of solids, and that increased susceptibility to attack by micro-organisms may be an important factor. A significant proportion of the fish used in the experiments developed fin rot, the caudal fin being most frequently affected. The controls did not develop this disease.

The laboratory work just described was followed by a study of the trout population of some streams in Cornwall polluted by china-clay wastes[10]. Ten sites were picked on unpolluted reaches of the rivers Tresilian, Par, Far and Camel, and 13 sites on polluted reaches of the Par, the Far and a tributary of the Camel. At each site a length of river having a surface area of 1,000–5,000 ft.^{2} was enclosed by stopnets of $\frac{1}{2}$ in. mesh; fish were caught from within these areas with electric fishing gear, and population estimates made. Some significant differences were seen in the trout population density; thus at seven polluted sites on the Par the fish numbered 2–5 per 1,000 ft.^{2}, whereas on the same river the unpolluted sites had fish densities of 16–27 per 1,000 ft.^{2}. To some extent these differences appeared to be associated with differences in the available food supply, for a study of the density of the invertebrate stream-bed population showed that great differences existed, particularly in the Par, between the quantity of bottom fauna at polluted and unpolluted sites. Nevertheless examination showed that the fish caught in the polluted reaches had well-filled stomachs, in spite of the turbidity of the water which must have impaired their vision, and their size and condition did not differ significantly from those of the control fish.

The polluted reaches of the Par carried up to 7,470 p.p.m. of suspended solids, an amount much greater than that used in the experimental study. The gills of several trout from the polluted rivers were examined and about 20 per cent showed thickening or fusion of the gill lamellae. The general conclusion to be drawn from the field study is that trout can live in rivers heavily polluted by china-clay wastes, but in much reduced numbers.

A new investigation has been carried out into the possible effects of coal-washing wastes and suspensions of wood fibres[11]. Large tanks of 350 l. capacity were used for these experiments. Near the bottom of each tank a two-bladed paddle rotated at 40 rev/min, preventing the suspended matter from settling; the fish in the upper part of the tank were protected from the paddle by a plastic-covered mesh of expanded metal. In addition to preventing the suspended matter from settling the rotating blades imparted a circular motion to the water so that the fish had to keep swimming to maintain position. Yearling rainbow trout were used in all the experiments—25 in each tank.

The fish survived control conditions, 50 p.p.m. and 100 p.p.m. of wood fibre for 7 months, but there was·a substantial mortality at 200 p.p.m.; about 50 per cent had died after 12 weeks, nearly all with symptoms of fin rot. The coal washings, however, appeared to be harmless. No fish died in any of the concentrations tested—50, 100 and 200 p.p.m.; all remained in excellent physical condition. This result is in contrast with the field study of Pautzke[1], but, as noted earlier, the washings in this case included sand and slate.

In the manufacture of phosphoric acid and superphosphate, calcium sulphate or gypsum, $CaSO_4 2H_2O$, is produced as a waste and considerable quantities of this may be discharged into estuaries[11]. The solubility of gypsum is rather limited and if the amount present is appreciably more than 2,000 p.p.m. some will be present as a suspension. Tests with solutions and solution-suspensions containing 1,000–10,000 p.p.m. of gypsum have been made, using rainbow trout and apparatus similar to that used in the experiments with wood fibres and coal washings. All the fish survived 28 days at concentrations of 1,000–3,163 p.p.m. The 28-day test period was chosen because migratory fish take about this time to travel up or down an estuary. At concentrations above 3,163 p.p.m., with considerable quantities of the gypsum in suspension, there were some deaths. Some of these, however, were the result of fighting. The general conclusion seems to be that calcium sulphate effluents do not present a serious hazard to fish in estuaries except, perhaps, in the immediate vicinity of the effluent outfall.

REFERENCES

[1] Pautzke, C. F.   Studies on the effect of coal washings on steelhead and cutthroat trout.   *Trans. Amer. Fish. Soc.*, 67 (1937) 232–3

[2] Cole, A. E.   Water pollution studies in Wisconsin.   Effects of industrial (pulp and papermill) wastes on fish.   *Sewage Wks J.*, 7 (1935) 280–302

[3] Griffin, L. D.   Turbidity as a factor in the decline of Great Lake fishes, with special reference to Lake Erie.   *Trans. Amer. Fish. Soc.*, 75 (1945) 281–322

[4] Larsen, K. and Olsen, S.   Ochre suffocation of fish in the River Tim Aa.   *Rep. Danish biol. Sta.*, 50 (1950) 3–27

[5] Paul, R. M.   Water pollution: a factor modifying fish populations in Pacific Coast streams.   *Sci. Mon., N.Y.*, 74 (1952) 14–17

[6] Wallen, I. E.   The direct effect of turbidity on fishes.   *Bull. Okla. agric. mech. Coll., Biol. Ser.*, 48 (1951) 27 pp.

[7] Bartsch, A. F.   Settleable solids, turbidity, and light penetration as factors affecting water quality.   In *Biological Problems in Water Pollution, Trans. 1959 Seminar Robert A. Taft Sanit. Eng. Cent. Tech. Rep. W60-3,* Cincinnati (1960)

[8] Stuart, T. A.   Spawning migration, reproduction and young stages of loch trout (*Salmo trutta* L.).   *Scottish Home Dept., Freshw. Salmon Fish. Res. Ser.*, 5 (1953) 39 pp.

[9] Herbert, D. W. M. and Merkens, J. C.   The effect of suspended mineral solids on the survival of trout.   *Int. J. Air Wat. Poll.*, 5 (1961) 46–55

[10] *Water Pollution Research, 1960.*   1961.   London; H.M.S.O.

[11] *Water Pollution Research, 1961.*   1962.   London; H.M.S.O.

15

THE TOXICITY OF COMPLEX EFFLUENTS

MANY polluting effluents are of complex composition, containing two, three or more toxic substances, and experimental work dealing with their effects presents special problems. Two toxic substances present in the same solution may have a combined effect which is additive; they may appear to interfere with one another, producing the condition known as antagonism, or their combined action may be greater than the sum of their separate effects—this is the condition known as synergism and is much rarer than antagonism.

When the combined effect of two substances is additive each exerts its action just as if the other were not present. If X_T and Y_T are the respective threshold concentrations, and X_S and Y_S are the concentrations of substances X and Y in the solution, then solutions containing both X and Y are not toxic when $X_S/X_T + Y_S/Y_T$ is not greater than unity. Such a case has already been considered in Chapter 12, that of ammonia and monohydric phenols. Another case recently investigated is that of zinc sulphate and ammonium chloride, two substances which may occur together in sewage effluents[1]. In *Figure 62* survival curves are drawn showing the toxicity to rainbow trout of solutions of ammonium chloride and of zinc sulphate. The concentrations are expressed as multiples of the threshold values, i.e. as Z_S/Z_T and A_S/A_T, where Z_S and A_S are the concentrations of zinc sulphate and ammonium chloride, and Z_T and A_T are the thresholds. It will be noticed that the slope of the ammonium chloride curve is much steeper than that of the zinc curve, the survival times shortening much more rapidly as the concentration increases. When curves are drawn in which the survival times are plotted against the actual concentrations in p.p.m. of zinc and N it is found that they cross at about 30 p.p.m. The threshold for ammonium chloride (in p.p.m. N) is a little less than this; the threshold for zinc is about 3·5 p.p.m.

Points are plotted in *Figure 62* showing the results of survival time experiments with mixtures. One series in which the $Z_S/Z_T : A_S/A_T$ ratio is 1:2 lies near the ammonium chloride curve; the other series in which the ratio is 2:1 lies nearer the zinc curve. The points for all the mixtures show that the solutions are not toxic when $A_S/A_T + Z_S/Z_T$ is not greater than 1. Theoretically the same method of predicting the toxicity of mixtures should be applicable to solutions of 3, 4 or more substances if their action is additive, but no experiments appear to have been carried out to test the applicability of the formula to more than two poisons.

When the effect of a toxic substance is reduced on the addition of another substance antagonism is said to exist. The reaction may take three forms: (1) The toxicity of a dissolved substance may be reduced

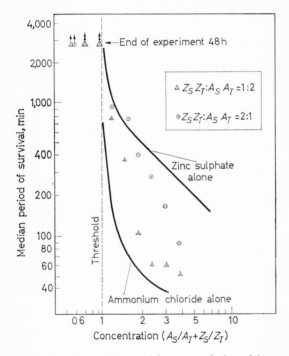

Figure 62. The toxicity to rainbow trout of zinc sulphate, ammonium chloride and mixtures of the two salts

(From Herbert[1], by courtesy of the Society for Water Treatment and Examination.

on the addition of a second substance not in itself toxic or not even soluble; (2) The addition of a second toxic substance reduces the effect of the first, but the action is not reciprocal; that is, no amount of the first substance will lessen the effect of the second, when this is present in sufficient quantity to be toxic; and (3) Two toxic substances in mixed solution are reciprocally antagonistic, each reducing the toxicity of the other. All three types of antagonism were discovered over 60 years ago. The first type seems to have been discovered by Naegeli[2] who found that the lethal effect on the worm *Tubifex* of water distilled in copper stills could be dispelled by the addition of small quantities of charcoal or sulphur. The toxic properties of such distilled water are probably due to traces of colloidal copper, and the action of the charcoal or sulphur was probably the removal of the copper by adsorption. The second type of antagonism was first described by Ringer and Phear[3] who showed that the toxicity of distilled water to

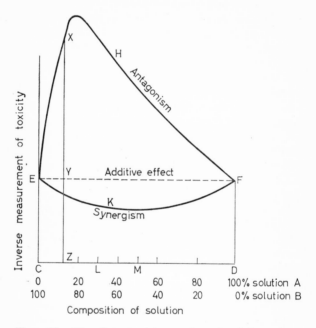

*Figure 63. The effect of mixing equally toxic solutions of two
substances in varying proportions*

(By courtesy of the *Journal of Experimental Biology*.)

tadpoles could be annulled by the addition of small quantities of potassium cyanide or potassium oxalate, and it seems probable that in this case the underlying principle is the precipitation of colloidal copper by electrolytes. The third type of antagonism is the best known and most studied; the literature dealing with it is considerable, and dates back to the classic work of Ringer[4] dealing with the physiological balance between calcium and potassium necessary for the working of the heart of vertebrate animals. Many theories have been put forward to explain this type of antagonism but a discussion of them would be beyond the scope of this chapter.

When it is necessary to determine by experiment whether antagonism exists between two toxic substances two methods of experiment can be employed:

(1) The method devised by Osterhout[5, 6] consists of determining the effect of mixtures, in various proportions, of equally toxic solutions of the two substances in question (*Figure 63*). A curve is worked out in which some inverse measurement of the toxicity, such as the survival time, is plotted as ordinate, and the composition of the mixture is plotted as abscissa. Thus at C the solution is 100 per cent B, at D it is 100 per cent A; at L the test solution is a mixture 30 per cent A and 70 per cent B; M represents a 50/50 mixture, etc. If the effect of the two substances is additive the survival times will lie along the line EF; the various mixtures will have the same toxicity as either of the two components. If antagonism exists the survival curve will rise between E and F, taking a form such as EHF. Usually the curve rises to some well-defined maximum; at any point the degree of antagonism may be measured as the ratio XY/YZ. The method was used by Osterhout to study the effect of electrolytes on algal cells and has not been used in work on fish. The writer has shown that the method can be used for work on animals; using tadpoles as test animals a marked antagonism between nickel and strontium can be demonstrated. For example, 0·015 N nickel nitrate and 0·23 N strontium nitrate are equally toxic, the survival time being about 100 min. Mixing the two solutions in 60:40 ratio results in the survival time going up to over 300 min[7].

(2) A series of solutions is prepared in which the concentration of one substance is maintained at a fixed value while that of the second substance is varied from zero up to some suitable maximum. A survival curve is worked out for this range of solutions and when antagonism is present it is found that the survival time lengthens as the concentration of the second substance increases. In *Figure 64* a series of survival curves shows the effect of sodium chloride on the toxicity of mercuric chloride to the minnow. It will be seen that at each concentration of mercuric chloride the addition of sodium chloride brings about a prolongation of the survival time, the antagonistic effect beginning at about 0·005 M NaCl and rising to a maximum at about 0·15 M. Above this value the survival curves fall sharply as the NaCl becomes toxic. The reaction involves three variables—the mercuric chloride concentration, the sodium chloride concentration and the survival time—and so the survival curve is

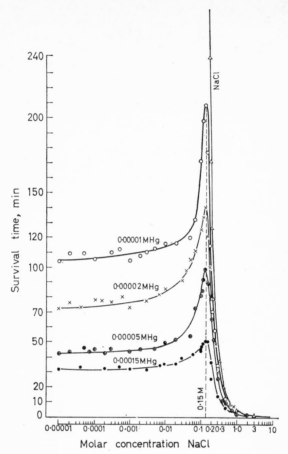

Figure 64. Survival curves for minnows in solutions of mercuric chloride and sodium chloride. The concentration of mercuric chloride in the mixtures is indicated by the figures inserted on the curves; that of the sodium chloride is given by the horizontal scale. Each plotted point represents the mean survival time of three fish. Temperature 16° C

(By courtesy of the *Journal of Experimental Biology*.)

really a curved surface. The survival curve peaks when the solutions are approximately isotonic, i.e. have an osmotic pressure equal to that of the body fluids of the animal, for the osmotic pressure of a 0·15 M solution of NaCl is about 6½ atm. A similar antagonistic effect is produced if glucose is used instead of sodium chloride which suggests that the basis of the reaction is osmotic. Another example of this method of demonstrating antagonism has been given in *Figure 24*, which shows the effect of calcium on the toxicity of lead nitrate.

There are two methods of detecting synergism between two toxic substances. The first again consists of measuring the toxicity of a series of mixtures of solutions of equal toxicity; when synergism is present the mixtures will be more toxic than the pure solutions and the survival curve will take a form like *EKF* in *Figure 63*. The second

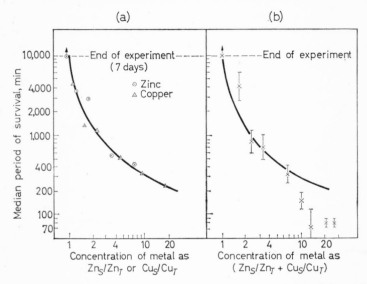

Figure 65.   Survival curves for rainbow trout in solutions of zinc sulphate and copper sulphate: (a) zinc and copper singly, (b) mixture of zinc and copper in the ratio 6:1.   Hardness of water 15–20 mg/l. as CaCO$_3$.   Temperature 17–18° C

method is used by Lloyd[8] in his study of the toxicity of mixtures of zinc sulphate and copper sulphate to the rainbow trout.   Lloyd shows that when survival times are plotted for zinc and copper with the concentrations expressed in multiples of the thresholds, i.e. as Zn_S/Zn_T or Cu_S/Cu_T, the same curve will fit both data [*Figure 65(a)*] which suggests that both salts exert their action in a similar way.   If their combined effect in mixtures were additive one would expect a survival curve for the mixtures, in which survival times are plotted against values of $Zn_S/Zn_T + Cu_S/Cu_T$, to follow much the same course as that for the salts taken singly, but this does not happen.   At the higher values of $Zn_S/Zn_T + Cu_S/Cu_T$ the mixtures are much more toxic than the single salt solutions [*Figure 65(b)*] which suggests the presence of synergism. These results were obtained with soft water solutions and in the mixtures the zinc:copper ratio was 6:1. Why this particular ratio should have been chosen is not clear; the thresholds are stated to be 0·56 p.p.m. for zinc and 0·044 p.p.m. for copper. Other studies of synergism and antagonism have shown that the degree of synergism or antagonism produced may vary considerably with the proportions in which the two toxic substances are present. Lloyd also carried out some experiments on the combined effect of zinc and copper in solutions made up with a hard water, and in this case no synergism was evident. In the use of hard water a considerable complication is introduced because the toxicity of zinc and copper is reduced by calcium.

When a polluting effluent is of complex and uncertain composition it is more or less futile to attempt estimates of its toxicity by making analyses and searching the literature for data on the toxicity of its components. Tests of the toxicity of the entire effluent at various dilutions are more useful, but care should be taken to use for dilution a water of the same nature as that present in the stream into which the effluent runs; otherwise the results may be misleading. The value of the tests will also depend very greatly on the degree to which the effluent is stable in composition and concentration. A typical effluent of complex and uncertain make-up is that discharged from kraft mills. This may contain sodium sulphide, hydrogen sulphide, methyl mercaptan, resin, fatty acids and their salts. Alderdice and Brett[9] have studied the toxicity of a full-bleach kraft mill effluent to Pacific salmon. Their assays were carried out with a 24 h composite sample of the effluent diluted with sea-water to concentrations of 2, 5, 6, 7, 8·5, 10 and 18 per cent by volume. A survival curve is drawn in which the harmonic mean survival time is plotted against the effluent concentration in per cent by volume. The survival time data show that a 4·8 per cent concentration appears to be about the limit of toxicity.

The reactions of the fish in dilutions of a complex effluent near the threshold may give some indication of the chief toxic substance at work. Thus very rapid and laboured breathing without early loss of balance might suggest heavy metal salts, acids or lack of oxygen; symptoms like anaesthesia, with loss of balance, loss of movement and very slow respiration would suggest cyanide or sulphide; wild movements, with very early loss of balance and flickering respiration, might indicate phenolic substances, and sudden death with gaping mouth and gill covers, ammonia. More experimental work is necessary on the reactions of fish to poisons and mixtures of poisons. A great deal

THE TOXICITY OF COMPLEX EFFLUENTS

of work on the effect of toxic substances on fish is limited to tolerance determinations: the fish are placed in a series of solutions and no observations are made on them until the time comes when the percentage of survivors has to be reckoned. As a result many papers dealing with the toxicity of pollutants to fish give little or no account of their symptoms.

An example of a complex effluent for which a complete analysis is available is that studied by Alabaster[10]. The analysis, tabulated below, shows that many toxic substances were present, including ammonia, synthetic detergents, phenols, cyanide, copper and zinc. Although so many poisons were present the essential factor determining the survival of fish in the effluent channel was the oxygen concentration.

Organic carbon	24 p.p.m.
Suspended solids	38 ,,
5 day B.O.D. as O_2	19 ,,
Permanganate value	22 ,,
Ammonia (as N)	28 ,,
Nitrite (as N)	1 ,,
Nitrate (as N)	55 ,,
Organic matter in suspended solids	74 per cent
pH	6·9 ,,
Synthetic detergent (as Mannoxol)	4·5 p.p.m.
Total phenols as C_6H_5OH	5·0 ,,
Monohydric phenols	0·7 ,,
Cyanide	0·04 ,,
Thiocyanate	0·025 ,,
Iron	1·2 ,,
Copper	0·15 ,,
Nickel	0·05 ,,
Zinc	0·2 ,,
Chromium	0·02 ,,
Manganese	trace

There is evidence that the low dissolved oxygen concentrations which are found in many polluted rivers increase the toxicity of many poisons to fish. Lloyd[11] has pointed out that the most obvious reaction of a fish to an insufficient oxygen supply is to increase the volume of water passing over its gills, and this may increase the amount of poison reaching the surface of the gill epithelium, the site at which most poisons are absorbed. There is some evidence also, that in fish, as in mammals, anoxia is followed by a rise of blood pressure and a quickening of the heartbeat[12]. An increase in the amount of blood passing through the gills and an increase in its rate of circulation around the body may be, to some extent, responsible for the more rapid effect of poisons under conditions of oxygen deficiency. Laboratory tests of the toxicity of effluents are generally made with well-aerated water, and when the oxygen content of the affected watercourse is low, this must be allowed for. Alderdice and Brett in their study of the effects of kraft mill effluents discussed above, consider that though a 4·8 per cent dilution of the effluent appeared to be safe under laboratory conditions, 2·5 per cent would be a safer limit, taking into account the possibility of respiratory difficulties.

Beak[13] considers that too much must not be expected from laboratory tests and that field tests should be carried out as well. Field tests of the toxicity of complex effluents may take various forms; fish may be confined in cages in the stream or effluent channel, or they may be kept in aquaria near the channel and arrangements can be made for the effluent or polluted stream water to flow through the aquaria. Allan, Alabaster and Herbert[14] tried out both these methods in a study of pollution in the River Colne in Hertfordshire, and found that the survival of fish in aquaria supplied with effluent was very similar to that of fish confined in live-boxes in the stream. The boxes in the stream proved to be much easier to install and maintain.

When a complex effluent runs into a comparatively small stream it will be diluted to a slight extent at first, but as the stream receives more and more tributaries or joins a larger watercourse the dilution becomes greater. Thus it is possible to set up a series of field experiments in which various dilutions of the effluent are tested. The degree of dilution may be measured by analysis, or by measuring the rates of flow. The experimenter must be prepared for complications, for the toxicity of the effluent may be altered by aeration in its passage down the stream, volatile substances may be lost, a heavy plant growth may remove some compounds, and the chemical nature of the diluting waters must be checked. Clemens and Summers[15] studied a complex effluent from an oil refinery, which was progressively diluted in this way down to about 4·5 per cent of its original concentration. They do not seem to have used fish cages, but simply filled 5 quart jars at each station and put two fish in each, keeping them under observation for a week. This type of experiment does not seem to have much advantage over a laboratory test with various concentrations of the neat effluent, though it may be argued that the field experiment can show up the changes in toxicity brought about by factors other than dilution.

Another method of field experiment consists of trapping and marking fish, which are replaced in the effluent channel or polluted stream. After a suitable time interval the traps can be used again, when records can be made of the movements of marked fish that are recaptured, their amount of growth, etc. Interesting new methods of investigating

THE TOXICITY OF COMPLEX EFFLUENTS

the long-term effects of pulp-mill waste on fish include tests in artificial streams, and in small natural streams artificially contaminated with controlled amounts of effluent.

REFERENCES

[1] Herbert, D. W. M. Freshwater fisheries and pollution control. *Proc. Soc. Water Treatm. & Examin.*, 10 (1961) 135–61
[2] Naegeli, C. v. Ueber oligodynamische Erscheinungen in lebenden Zellen. *Denkschr. schweiz. naturf. Ges.*, 33 (1893) 1
[3] Ringer, S. and Phear, A. G. The action of distilled water on *Tubifex*. *J. Physiol.*, 17 (1895) 423
[4] Ringer, S. On the mutual antagonism between lime and potash salts in toxic doses. *J. Physiol.*, 5 (1884) 247
[5] Osterhout, W. J. V. The measurement of antagonism. *Bot. Gaz.*, 58 (1914) 272–6
[6] Osterhout, W. J. V. Quantitative criteria of antagonism. *Bot. Gaz.*, 58 (1914) 178–86
[7] Jones, J. R. E. Antagonism between salts of the heavy and alkaline-earth metals in their toxic action on the tadpole of the toad, *Bufo bufo bufo* (L.). *J. exp. Biol.*, 16 (1939) 313–33
[8] Lloyd, R. The toxicity of mixtures of zinc and copper sulphates to rainbow trout (*Salmo gairdnerii* Richardson). *Ann. appl. Biol.*, 49 (1961) 535–8
[9] Alderdice, D. F. and Brett, J. R. Some effects of kraft mill effluent on young Pacific salmon. *J. Fish. Res. Bd Can.*, 14 (1957) 783–95
[10] Alabaster, J. S. The effect of a sewage effluent on the distribution of dissolved oxygen and fish in a stream. *J. Anim. Ecol.*, 28 (1959) 283–91
[11] Lloyd, R. Effect of dissolved oxygen concentrations on the toxicity of several poisons to rainbow trout (*Salmo gairdnerii* Richardson). *J. exp. Biol.*, 38 (1961) 447–55
[12] Mott, J. C. The cardiovascular system. In *The Physiology of Fishes, Volume 1—Metabolism*, ed. by Margeret E. Brown. 1957. New York; Academic Press
[13] Beak, T. W. Toleration of fish to toxic pollution. *J. Fish. Res. Bd Can.*, 15 (1958) 559–72
[14] Allan, I. R. H., Alabaster, J. S. and Herbert, D. W. M. Recent studies on toxicity and stream pollution. *Wat. Sanit. Engr.*, 5 (1954) 109–12
[15] Clemens, H. P. and Summers, P. B. A phase in managing refinery wastes polluting streams. *Proc. Okla. Acad. Sci.*, 33 (1952) 86–96
[16] Jones, J. R. E. The toxicity of the double chlorides of mercury and sodium, I. Experiments with the minnow *Phoxinus phoxinus* (L.). *J. exp. Biol.*, 17 (1940) 325–30

16

THE EFFECTS OF POLLUTION ON FISH EGGS

IN this last chapter the effects of pollution on the eggs of fish are examined. The problem has not been given a great deal of study and the information available applies almost entirely to the salmonidae. This, in some ways, is a little surprising, for more than 60 years ago it was discovered that fish eggs were a very satisfactory biological material for the study of the effects of toxic solutions. Much of the classic work of Loeb[1] on physiologically balanced salt solutions was carried out with fish eggs and Mathews' work[2] on the relative toxicity of the metals was done with the eggs of the mud-minnow or killifish. Mathews found that the toxicity of a salt could be estimated by putting eggs into solutions of graded concentration and observing the minimum concentration at which development of the embryo was prevented. Another study on these lines is that of Chace and Gies[3]. None of this work has much bearing on the study of water pollution; as far as they go these early studies of the toxic effects of salts and other substances on fish eggs have shown that the eggs are much more resistant than the adult fish. Thus Mathews found the toxicity thresholds for lead, zinc and nickel to be about 20, 40 and 2,000 p.p.m. respectively, values far higher than those found for the adult animal.

There has been some study of the range of hydrogen ion concentration within which the hatching of the eggs will take place. Krishna[4] has studied the effect of pH changes on developing trout ova, using tap-water acidified with HCl or made alkaline with NaOH. He found that the eggs would develop normally between pH 4–5 on the acid side and 8–9 on the alkaline side. In water more acid than pH 4·0, the eggs displayed exosmosis and collapsed; in water more alkaline than pH 9·0 there was endosmosis, the eggs swelled and the yolk became white. According to Smith[5] salmon and trout ova swell for some time after being set free, until the chorion is stretched to form a hard and rigid structure and a considerable hydrostatic pressure is established within it. The egg is relatively impermeable to salts at this time, but the chorion permits the passage of ammonia and hydrogen and hydroxyl ions.

Some information on the effects of tar substances on trout ova is given in the 1930 Government report dealing with road-surfacing materials[6]. Phenol, quinoline, naphthalene and acridine were used for tests in which newly extruded milt and ova were treated for 15 min with 10 cm^3 of the test solution, the solution being thoroughly mixed into the egg mass with the finger. After the 15 min treatment the eggs were washed with hatchery water and placed on glass grilles in wooden hatching troughs supplied with a good flow of spring water. The results were rather inconsistent in some cases; thus in one series 93 per cent of the eggs hatched to healthy alevins after treatment with a saturated solution of naphthalene, while 16 per cent hatched in a half-saturated solution and only 9 per cent in one a quarter saturated. The general result of the whole series, however, was fairly definite. The eggs were much more resistant than the fish; for example, whereas a 20 p.p.m. phenol solution is fatal to an adult fish in about 1 h, 95 per cent of a batch of eggs will hatch after treatment with a solution of this concentration. It should be noted, however, that the eggs were exposed to the solution for 15 min only.

Most studies of the possible effects of pollution on the eggs of fish have been concerned with the available oxygen supply in spawning beds and the extent to which this may be affected by pollution and the deposition of silt. A fish, by adjusting its rate and depth of breathing, can compensate, to some extent at least, for deficiencies in the oxygen supply and at the worst can move away to seek better-aerated water. The egg in the gravel bed obviously has no control over the available oxygen supply and so the amount brought to it in the water flowing through the gravel is a factor of critical importance. According to Stuart[7] the female trout will select a spot for spawning where the water is not too fast running, and where the gravel is composed of stones up to 3 in. in diameter, with a large proportion of materials of a type suitable to consolidate the mass while leaving it freely permeable to the water. Stones embedded in fine sand or silt are avoided, as are uniform gravels and shingles which move easily in a flood. The location of the redds in an ideal pool is towards the 'tail' where the gravel slopes gently upwards and where there is an acceleration of the current leading to the next pool or riffle. Stuart was able to demonstrate the presence of water currents in the ova pockets by injecting potassium permanganate into the gravel to depths of 6–8 in. The coloured solution emerged from the gravel beyond the ova pockets; crystals of permanganate placed on the stones disappeared almost immediately without trace. However, all trout cannot have access to ideal places for spawning and some will deposit ova in places where there is little chance of their survival. Jones and Ball[8] have shown that in a tank a female trout will excavate a hole in the gravel, at the bottom of which there is hardly any movement of the water.

Stuart[7] found that when fertilized trout ova are placed in dishes which are heavily charged with sediment the ova seem to attract the fine particles, and the smooth and glossy chorion may become completely covered with a dark accumulation which can only be dislodged by vigorous stirring. Early ova which get into this condition fail to hatch but eyed ova may hatch to healthy alevins. Stuart did not measure the oxygen consumption of the eggs, and the extent to which this is altered by a deposition of silt is not known; his observations on the reactions of the alevins to the presence of silt have been described in Chapter 14. Hayes, Wilmot and Livingstone[9] have made a study of the oxygen consumption of salmon eggs and have

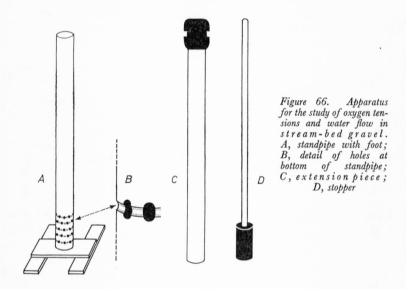

Figure 66. Apparatus for the study of oxygen tensions and water flow in stream-bed gravel. A, standpipe with foot; B, detail of holes at bottom of standpipe; C, extension piece; D, stopper

shown that at every stage in embryology there is a certain critical value for the oxygen tension of the water; above the critical value the consumption remains constant, at tensions below it the oxygen consumption is subnormal. The critical tension is about 40 mm Hg for newly fertilized eggs and rises, as the embryo develops, to about 100 mm Hg (about 60 per cent saturation) at the time of hatching. In a temporary subjection to a reduced oxygen concentration the developing ova cannot acquire an oxygen debt, so that when the available supply of oxygen is insufficient a slowing-up of development is inevitable.

The basic apparatus devised for the study of oxygen tensions and water flow in stream-bed gravel is shown in *Figure 66*. *A* is an aluminium 'standpipe' which measures about 15 in. by $1\frac{1}{4}$ in. It has a foot to anchor it firmly in the stream-bed in a vertical position, the foot being about 10 in. below the surface of the gravel. Its lower end is perforated with a number of one-eighth inch holes, and these are connected by annular external grooves one-sixteenth inch wide (*B*), which help to prevent the holes being blocked by the pebbles. Water can be prevented from flowing through the standpipe, if necessary, by inserting the stopper *D*. When the pipe is left in the stream-bed its upper end is closed by a rubber cap; when measurements of the intra-gravel conditions are to be made this cap is removed and the extension pipe *C* is fitted so as to bring the access to the interior of the pipe above the surface of the water. The rate of flow of the water in the gravel can be estimated by injecting a coloured solution; as the water flows through the gravel the colour of samples taken from the pipe will fade. By periodic sampling the apparent velocity of the water in the gravel may be estimated [10].

Using apparatus of this type Wickett[11] studied conditions in a stream in which there was a high mortality of chum salmon eggs. Wickett concluded that the three important factors determining survival were the number of eggs in the egg mass, the oxygen tension of the water and its rate of flow. High mortality might be the result of very low oxygen content, low water velocity or a combination of both. Coble[12] has made a study of the way spawning conditions affect the survival of steelhead trout ova and his data (*Figure 67*) also show that percentage survival is related to water velocity and oxygen tension. Coble cites the work of Shumway[13] who found that the embryo's oxygen requirements can be met by very low water velocities when the oxygen tension is adequate. This view was not shared by Wickett[11] who concluded that even air-saturated water cannot sustain the life of the egg if the water velocity is very low.

It is evident that oxygen shortage due to a low oxygen tension in the water flowing through the gravel, an insufficient rate of flow or a combination of both these adverse factors will hold up the development of fish eggs, delay hatching or, perhaps, prove fatal to the embryos. Alderdice, Wickett and Brett[14] have carried out a laboratory study of the effects of temporary exposures to low oxygen tensions on the eggs of the chum salmon. Deoxygenated water was prepared with vertical columns filled with glass chips, the water passing downwards and a stream of nitrogen passing upwards. The eggs were not exposed to the low oxygen tensions for the whole period of development but each batch was placed in water of low oxygen tension for a period of seven days, this period beginning 12, 20, 30 or 45 days after fertilization. So as to take count of both time and temperature the developmental stages are timed in degree-days; thus, for example, when development has gone on for 10 days at 10° C the stage is 100 degree-days.

The results of four series of experiments are shown in *Figure 68*. In the 121·2 degree-day series the lowest oxygen concentrations (0·29 and 0·25 p.p.m.) appeared responsible not only for a delay in hatching of about 10 days but also for the production of a very high proportion of monstrosities, abnormal alevins characterized by a shortening of the

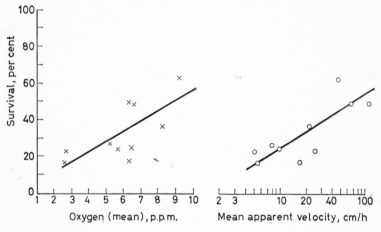

Figure 67. Per cent survival of embryo trout correlated with dissolved oxygen content (left) and with mean apparent water velocity (right). Each point represents the result of an experiment in which 100 eggs, with a suitable amount of gravel, were placed in a plastic mesh sack in a bed of spawning gravel. Standpipe apparatus as shown in Figure 66 was used to determine water conditions, and the surviving fry were counted one month after the calculated hatching time

(Drawn from the data of Coble[12].)

vertebral column posteriorly. Some were so truncated that the caudal fin was located immediately behind the dorsal fin. In the 205·8 and 296·1 degree-day experiments the chief result of oxygen deficiency was delayed hatching but in the 205·8 degree-day series it is not at all clear just where, on the concentration scale, the delay begins since no experiments were carried out between 1·67 and 10·2 p.p.m. In the 296·1 series the slope of the left limb of the graph seems to suggest that delay begins at about 4 p.p.m. At the lowest levels in both these series there was a high mortality, and the short vertical bars in *Figure 68* mark the oxygen concentrations at which 50 per cent of the eggs died. In the 452·4 degree-day series there was a tendency to premature hatching at 0·8 p.p.m.; none of the alevins lived. At the next oxygen concentration in this series (1·81 p.p.m.) all the eggs hatched to live alevins.

The period of exposure to low oxygen tensions in these experiments amounts to only about one-seventh of the incubation time of controls,

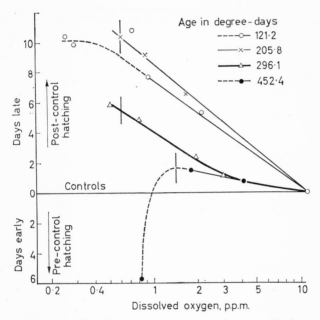

Figure 68. The effect of seven-day exposures to low-oxygen levels on the hatching of chum salmon eggs. The developmental stage at which the seven-day exposure to oxygen-deficient water was begun is indicated in degree-days (product of temperature and time of development). Points above the control line indicate delayed hatching; the point below the line records a premature hatching. Short vertical bars indicate 50 per cent lethal levels

(Drawn from the data of Alderdice, Wickett and Brett [14].)

and the effects of low oxygen tensions for the whole period of development were not examined. It may be presumed that any concentration below the critical level must slow up the speed of embryology. A further study by Alderdice and Wickett[15] deals with the effect of carbon dioxide on developing chum salmon eggs. The fertilized eggs were placed, in batches of 50, in water containing about 2·5 p.p.m. of oxygen and 6·5, 124, 203 and 243 p.p.m. of carbon dioxide. The results (*Figure 69*) show that a marked decline in the percentage hatch sets in somewhere between 6·5 and 124 p.p.m. CO_2. According to the interpolation of the results, based according to the authors on a probit plot, a 50 per cent survival should correspond to a CO_2 concentration of about 90 p.p.m., which is high. Another study of the effect of carbon dioxide on the development of fish eggs is that of

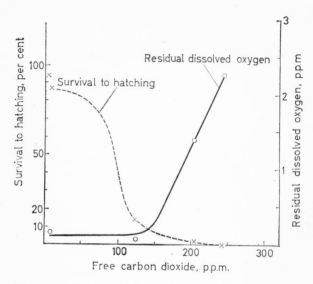

Figure 69. The effect of carbon dioxide on the utilization of dissolved oxygen by chum salmon eggs and the recorded percentage live hatch after exposure to 6·5, 124, 203 and 243 p.p.m. of carbon dioxide in closed bottles for nine days. Age of eggs at the beginning of the test, 14 days
(Drawn from the data of Alderdice and Wickett [15].)

Kelley [16]; in this case with a marine fish, the herring. Kelley found that concentrations of 7·52 to 67·76 p.p.m. had no apparent effect on the percentage of eggs surviving though there might be some re-tardation of development, due, perhaps to pH changes.

It would appear that before a final assessment can be made regard-ing the effects of silting, oxygen deficiency, and excess of carbon dioxide on salmonid eggs some investigations should be made of the natural mortality of the eggs under average conditions. Following the normal processes of limitation of animal numbers some mortality must be expected. Stuart[7], experimenting with ova artificially fertilized and placed in cages of Perspex sheet, found a very low percentage of dead eggs—an average of 2·5 per cent in 7 cages, each containing 200 eggs. Unfortunately, attempts to count the alevins hatched were not successful.

REFERENCES

[1] Loeb, J. Studies on the physiological effects of the valency and possibly the electrical charges of ions. I. The toxic and antitoxic effects of ions as a function of their valency and possibly their electrical charge. *Amer. J. Physiol.*, 6 (1902) 411–33

[2] Mathews, A. P. The relation between solution tension, atomic volume, and the physiological action of the elements. *Amer. J. Physiol.*, 10 (1904) 290–323

[3] Chace, A. F. and Gies, W. J. Preliminary observations on the poisonous action of thorium. *Amer. J. Physiol.*, 18 (1907) 457

[4] Krishna, D. Effect of changing pH on developing trout eggs and larvae. *Nature, Lond.*, 171 (1953) 434

[5] Smith, S. Early development and hatching. In *The Physiology of Fishes, Volume 1—Metabolism*, ed. Margaret E. Brown. 1957. New York; Academic Press

[6] Ministry of Transport and Ministry of Agriculture and Fisheries. Detailed Biological and Chemical Reports on Tars used for Road-surfacing. 1930. London; H.M.S.O.

[7] Stuart, T. A. Spawning migration, reproduction and young stages of loch trout (*Salmo trutta* L.). *Scottish Home Dept., Freshw. Salmon Fish. Res. Ser.*, 5 (1953) 39 pp.

[8] Jones, J. W. and Ball, J. N. The spawning behaviour of brown trout and salmon. *Brit. J. anim. Behav.*, 2 (1954) 103–14

[9] Hayes, F. R., Wilmot, I. R. and Livingstone, D. A. The oxygen consumption of the salmon egg in relation to development and activity. *J. exp. Zool.*, 16 (1951) 377–95

[10] Terhune, L. D. B. The mark VI groundwater standpipe for measuring seepage through salmon spawning gravel. *J. Fish. Res. Bd Can.*, 15 (1958) 1027–63

[11] Wickett, W. P. The oxygen supply to salmon eggs in spawning beds. *J. Fish. Res. Bd Can.*, 11 (1954) 933–53

[12] Coble, D. W. Influence of water exchange and dissolved oxygen in redds on survival of steelhead trout embryos. *Trans. Amer. Fish. Soc.*, 90 (1961) 469–74

[13] Shumway, D. L. The influence of water velocity on the development of salmonid embryos at low oxygen levels. *M.Sc. thesis*, Oregon State College, Corvallis, U.S.A., 49 pp. (Cited by Coble[12])

[14] Alderdice, D. F., Wickett, W. P. and Brett, J. R. Some effects of temporary exposure to low oxygen levels on Pacific salmon eggs. *J. Fish. Res. Bd Can.*, 15 (1958) 229–49

[15] Alderdice, D. F. and Wickett, W. P. A note on the response of developing chum salmon eggs to free carbon dioxide in solution. *J. Fish. Res. Bd Can.*, 15 (1958) 797–99

[16] Kelley, A. M. Effect of abnormal CO_2 tension on development of herring eggs. *J. Fish. Res. Bd Can.*, 6 (1946) 435–40

APPENDIX

Check List of the Chief Fish used in Experimental Work on the Effect
of Pollutants and in Related Physiological Studies

Common name	Scientific name
Black bullhead	*Ameiurus melas* (Rafinesque)
Bleak	*Alburnus alburnus* (L.)
Bluegill	*Lepomis macrochirus* Rafinesque
Blunt-nosed minnow . . .	*Pimephales notatus* (Rafinesque)
Brook stickleback . . .	*Eucalia inconstans* (Kirtland)
Brown trout	*Salmo trutta* L.
Bullhead or catfish . . .	*Ameiurus nebulosus* (Le Sueur)
Carp	*Cyprinus carpio* L.
Channel cat or fiddler . .	*Ictalurus punctatus* (Rafinesque)
Chinook salmon	*Oncorhynchus tshawytscha* (Walbaum)
Chub	*Squalius cephalus* (L.)
Chum salmon	*Oncorhynchus keta* (Walbaum)
Coho (silver) salmon . .	*O. kisutch* (Walbaum)
Common sucker	*Catostomus commersonii* (Lacépède)
Creek chub	*Semotilus atromaculatus* (Mitchill)
Dace	*Leuciscus leuciscus* (L.)
Eel	*Anguilla anguilla* (L.)
Fathead minnow . . .	*Pimephales promelas* Rafinesque
Golden shiner	*Notemigonus crysoleucas* (Mitchill)
Goldfish (common) . . .	*Carassius auratus* (L.)
Goldfish (Crucian carp) . .	*Carassius carassius* (L.)
Guppy	*Lebistes reticulatus* (Peters)
Lake trout	*Salvelinus namaycush* (Walbaum)
Largemouth bass . . .	*Micropterus salmoides* (Lacépède)
Loach	*Nemacheilus barbatula* (L.)
Minnow	*Phoxinus phoxinus* L.
Mudminnow or mummichog .	*Fundulus heteroclitus* (L.)
Perch	*Perca fluviatilis* L.
Pike or northern pike . .	*Esox lucius* (L.)
Pink salmon	*Oncorhynchus gorbuscha* (Walbaum)
Plains killifish	*Fundulus kansae* Garman
Pumpkinseed	*Eupomotis gibbosus* (L.)
Rainbow trout	*Salmo gairdnerii* Richardson
Red horse	*Moxostoma aureolum* (Le Sueur)
Roach	*Rutilus rutilus* (L.)
Salmon (Atlantic) . . .	*Salmo salar* L.
Sculpin	*Cottus perplexus* Gilbert & Evermann
Sockeye salmon	*Oncorhynchus nerka* (Walbaum)
Speckled trout, brook trout or American char . .	*Salvelinus fontinalis* (Mitchill)
Stickleback (3-spined) . .	*Gasterosteus aculeatus* L.
Stickleback (12-spined) . .	*Pygosteus pungitius* L.
Straw-coloured minnow . .	*Notropis blennius* (Gir.)
Sunfish (common or orange-spotted)	*Lepomis humilis* Gir.
Tench	*Tinca tinca* (L.)
Wall eye	*Stizostedion vitreum* (Mitchill)
White crappie	*Pomoxis annularis* Rafinesque
Yellow perch	*Perca flavescens* (Mitchill)

AUTHOR INDEX

195

AUTHOR INDEX

197

Scott, W. J., 9, 24
Shelford, V. E., 1, 8, 17, 24, 27–8, 38,
    89, 96, 101–2, 104, 106, 114, 117,
    142–4, 152
Shelton, G., 24
Shumway, D. L., 189, 193
Sigler, W. F., 117
Smith, H. W., 71, 81
Smith, S., 186, 193
Smith, W. C., 56, 65
Sneed, K. E., 138, 141
Southgate, B. A., 84, 89, 95, 145, 152
Spaas, J. T., 168
Spoor, W. A., 8, 10, 24
Steinmann, P., 2, 4
Stiemke, R. E., 110, 116
Stringer, G. E., 131, 140
Stroede, W., 92, 96
Strong, E. R., 51
Stuart, T. A., 171, 175, 187–8, 192–3
Summers, P. B., 184–5
Sumner, F. B., 157, 167
Surber, E. W., 51, 128, 139

Tabata, K., 135, 140
Tarzwell, C. M., 73, 81, 132–5, 140
Terhune, L. D. B., 193
Thompson, D. H., 15, 25, 35
Trama, F. B., 73, 81, 147, 152
Trembley, F. J., 166–7
Truesdale, G. A., 166
Tyler, R. G., 106

Van Dam, L., 7, 12–14, 24, 98, 105
Van der Zee, H., 126
Vandyke, K. G., 166

Van Horn, W. M., 51
Van Oosten, J., 62, 65
Von Skramlik, E., 24

Walker, K. F., 157, 165–7
Wallen, I. E., 170–1, 175
Warren, C. E., 25–6, 35, 38
Warren, E., 45, 52
Washburn, G. N., 15, 25
Wasteneys, H., 156, 166
Weatherley, A. H., 106, 168
Weber, E., 73, 81
Weiss, C. M., 140
Welch, P. S., 107, 116
Wells, M. M., 76, 82, 98, 100, 105, 114,
    117
Wells, N. A., 1, 12, 24, 157, 167
Wells, W. H., 139
Westfall, B. A., 56, 65, 110, 113, 116
Westin, M. J., 106
Wheatland, A. B., 104, 106
Whitmore, C. M., 35, 37–8
Wickett, W. P., 189, 191, 192, 193
Wiebe, A. H., 5, 24, 37–8, 73, 81, 113,
    117
Wilding, J. L., 26
Williams, R. T., 86, 95
Wilmot, I. R., 188, 193
Wingfield, C. A., 165, 167
Woker, H., 51, 87, 95, 101, 106, 145,
    147, 152
Wright, S., 24, 38, 105
Wuhrmann, K., 39–40, 42, 47–8, 51,
    87–8, 95, 101, 106, 145, 147, 152

Zehender, F., 101, 106

SUBJECT INDEX

SUBJECT INDEX

China clay, 169, 173
Chloramines, 104
Chlordane, 131, 133
Chlorinated hydrocarbons, 130–33
Chlorine, 71, 103–4
Chloroform, 71, 85
Chlorophenol, effect on flavour of fish, 147
Chromates, 112
Chromium, 68–9, 112
'Closed chamber' experiments, 17, 99–100
Coagulation film anoxia, 56, 59, 61, 110, 169
Coal washing, 169–70, 174
Cobalt, 66–8, 73
Complex cyanides, 88–9
Co-ral, 135
Cresols, 2, 40, 142, 144–5, 147, 150–1
Criteria of time-effect relationship, 39–40
Cruising speed of fish, 22, 163
Cyanogen chloride, 104–5
Cytochrome system, 83

DDT, 129–31, 133
Delayed hatching of eggs, 189–92
Derris, 128
Diatomaceous earth, 172–3
Dieldrin, 131–3
Dipterex, 135
Disyston, 135
DNOC, 128, 142
DNOCHP, 128
'Drip', 142

Electricity generating plant, 154
Endrin, 133
  persistence of, 131
EPN, 135
Escape of fish from polluted water, 35, 76, 93
Ether, 71

Fatality curve, 45
Ferric chloride, 68–9
Ferric hydroxide, 69
Ferrous salts, effect on oxygen, 5, 69
Ferrous sulphate, 3

Field experiments
  aquaria, with, 184
  artificial streams, with, 185
  fish cages, with, 2, 15, 54, 130, 170, 184
  trapping and marking, 184
Fin rot, 173–4
Fish, suitability for experiment,
  American species, 42
  goldfish, 1, 41
  minnow, 1, 34, 41–2
  perch, 42
  roach, 42
  stickleback, 42
  trout (brown and rainbow), 42
  trout fry, 34
Fluorides, 113
Foam on rivers, 118
Formaldehyde, 71

Gas
  liquor, 142
  waste, toxicity of substances in, 143 (Table 11)
Gas-bubble disease, 28
Gills
  cyanide poisoning in, 84–5
  damage to, by,
    acids, 109
    detergents, 125
    grit, 54
    heavy metals, 56, 61–2, 64, 66, 73
    ochre, 170
    soaps, 125
    suspended matter, 169, 171, 173
  toxic substances, permeability to, 71
Gold, 66–7
Guaiacol, 145
Gut, damage by chromium, 112
Guthion, 135
Gypsum, 174

'Half-scope' standard, 23
Hard water, effect on toxicity of
  ammonium chloride, 101
  detergents, 122
  heavy metals, 59–61
  insecticides, 135
  soaps, 125
Hatcheries, zinc in, 57–9

SUBJECT INDEX

Heat death, 156, 161
Heat tolerance formula, 157
Heptachlor, 131, 133
Hydrogen sulphide, 5, 89–90
    concentrations detectable in air, 92
Hydrolysis, effect on toxicity of
    ammonium salts, 101
    cyanides, 87
    metallic salts, 68-9
    organic phosphates, 135

Ionization of detergents, 118–19
Iron pickle liquor, 107
Iron pollution from lignite pits, 170
Iron salts, 2
    (see also ferric and ferrous compounds)

Kaolin, 172–3
Kraft mill effluents, 182, 184

Lake Opeongo, 159
Lead mining, 53, 57
Lime, 113
Lindane, 133–4
Lissapol N, 118
Literature, abstracts and summaries, 4
Loch Leven, 108

Magnesium, 71, 73
Manganese, 66, 70, 73
Manifestation time, 40
Mercuric chloride, 67, 73, 78, 179–80
Mercury, 56, 66–7, 73
Methane, 105
Methoxychlor, 131, 133
Methyl mercaptan, 71, 182
Mine dumps, 54, 57
Mine-water pollution, 69
Mucus, coagulation of, by
    acids, 109
    coal washings, 170
    heavy metals, 55–6, 59, 61, 66
    iron-polluted water, 170
    quinoline, 145
    soaps, 125
Mucus secretions, functions of, 62

Naphthalene, 85, 143–4, 187
Narcosis, 145

'Nascent oxygen', 105
Nervous system, effect of organic phosphates, 135
Nickel, 66–8, 73, 179
    detoxification of cyanide, for, 88–9
Nicotine, 128
Nitrogen trichloride, 104

OMPA, 135
Organic phosphates, 135
Osmotic pressure, 66, 70–1
Overturning time, 40
Oxygen concentration
    asphyxial level, 21
    critical levels, 20, 21 (Table 4), 188, 191
    frozen lakes and rivers, of, 15
    level of no excess activity, 20–1
    limiting values for fish, 19 (Table 3)
        low temperatures, at, 16 (Table 2)
    oxykinetic level, 23
    residual level, 21
    salmon egg development, effect on, 189–91
    septic areas, of, 5
    spawning beds, in, 187
    suitable for fish life, 16
    swimming speed, effect on, 22
    thermal pollution, effect of, 161–2
    toxicity of cyanide, effect on, 87
    toxicity of poisons in general, effect on, 183
    various effluents, effect of, 5
Oxygen consumption
    activity, and, 11–12, 164
    temperature, effect of, 12, 164
    various animals, of, 11, 12 (Table 1)
Oxygen, solubility in water, 13
Ozone, 105

Para-oxon, 135
Parathion, 135
Permissible concentrations of pollutants, 51
pH
    changes, adjustment to, 111
    'closed chamber' experiments, in, 37
    effect on
        growth of fish, 107–8

201